D0501948

THE AUDUBON NATURE ENCYCLOPEDIA

CREATED AND PRODUCED BY
COPYLAB PUBLISHING COUNSEL, INC., NEW YORK

THE AUDUBON NATURE ENCYCLOPEDIA

SPONSORED BY THE NATIONAL AUDUBON SOCIETY

VOLUME 1

AC-BE

CURTIS BOOKS
A division of
The Curtis Publishing Company
Philadelphia – New York

First Printing
 Library of Congress Card Catalog Number 64-8877.

Published simultaneously in Canada by
Curtis Distributing Company, Ltd., Toronto.

Printed in the United States of America

EDITORIAL BOARD

CONSULTING EDITORS

CHARLES M. BOGERT
Chairman and Curator, Department of Reptiles and Amphibians, American Museum of Natural History

T. DONALD CARTER
Formerly Assistant Curator of Mammals, American Museum of Natural History

ALLAN D. CRUICKSHANK
Staff Photographer of the National Audubon Society; ornithologist, author, lecturer

ALICE GRAY
Specialist in Entomological Education; Scientific Assistant, Department of Entomology, American Museum of Natural History

ROGER TORY PETERSON
Artist, naturalist; Vice-president of the American Ornithologists' Union; former Member of the Board of Directors, National Audubon Society; author, *A Field Guide to the Birds* and many other books

OLIN SEWALL PETTINGILL
Director, Laboratory of Ornithology Cornell University; Secretary and Member of the Board of Directors, National Audubon Society

EDWIN WAY TEALE
Naturalist and author, *North with the Spring, Journey into Summer* and many other books

CONTRIBUTING AUTHORS

CYRIL E. ABBOTT —C.E.A.

ALEXANDER B. ADAMS, *Writer, Naturalist* —A.B.A.

ROBERT PORTER ALLEN, *Biologist, Formerly Director of Research, National Audubon Society* —R.P.A.

ALFRED M. BAILEY, *Director, Denver Museum of Natural History, Naturalist, Author, and National Audubon Society Lecturer* —A.M.B.

GERALD A. BAIR, *Editor, Writer* —G.A.B.

JOHN H. BAKER, *President Emeritus, National Audubon Society* —J.H.B.

CRAWFORD BENEDICT, *Author, Authority on Trees, Tree Surgeon* —C.B.

MICHAEL H. BEVANS, *Artist, Nature Writer* —M.H.B.

ANDREW BIHUN, Jr., *Naturalist* —A.B.,Jr.

MARK BOESCH —Mk.B.

CHARLES M. BOGERT, *Chairman and Curator, Department of Reptiles and Amphibians, The American Museum of Natural History* —C.M.B.

JAMES BOND, *Author* —J.B.

DONALD J. BORROR, *Zoologist, Entomologist* —D.J.B.

HERVEY BRACKBILL —H.B.

OSMOND P. BRELAND, *Professor of Zoology, University of Texas* —O.P.B.

CHARLES M. BROOKFLEID, *Naturalist, Florida Representative of The National Audubon Society* —Ch.B.

MAURICE BROOKS, *Professor of Wildlife Management, West Virginia University* —M.B.

CARL W. BUCHHEISTER, *President, National Audubon Society* —C.W.B.

PAUL BULLA —P.B.

ADA KNEALE BURNS, *Nature Educator* —A.K.B.

B. BARTRAM CADBURY, *Naturalist* —B.B.C.

JOSEPH CADBURY, *Naturalist* —J.C.

RACHEL CARSON, *Biologist, United States Government, Author,* Sea Around Us, Silent Spring —R.C.

T. DONALD CARTER, *Assistant Curator of Mammals, The American Museum of Natural History* —T.D.C.

AMY CLAMPITT, *Author* —Ay.C.

DONALD H. CLARK —D.H.C.

JOHN R. CLAWSON, *Photographer and Naturalist* —J.R.C.

ROLAND C. CLEMENT, *Staff Biologist, Director of Technical Studies, National Audubon Society* —R.C.C.

EDWIN H. COLBERT, *Curator of Fossil Reptiles and Amphibians, The American Museum of Natural History* —E.H.C.

ROBERT R. COLES, *Formerly Director, the Hayden Planetarium* —R.R.C.

ROGER CONNANT, *Curator of Reptiles, Philadelphia Zoological Garden* —Ro.C.

ALFRED M. COOPER —A.M.C.

CLARENCE COTTAM, *Chairman of the Executive Committee and Board of Trustees, National Park Association; Director, Welder Wildlife Foundation, Sintan, Texas* —C.C.

ARTHUR CRONQUIST, *Senior Curator, New York Botanical Garden* —A.C.

G. M. DAETZ —G.M.D.

JAY N. DARLING, *Winner, 1960 Audubon Medal* —J.N.D.

BARBARA DAVIS, *Writer, editor* —B.D.

JOHN V. DENNIS, *Naturalist* —J.V.D.

ALAN DEVOE, *Author* —A.D.

GEORGE DOCK, Jr., *Naturalist, Author, formerly Director of Public Relations, National Audubon Society* —G.D.,Jr.

RALPH J. and MILDRED L. DONAHUE, *Authors and Photographers* —R.J.D. and M.L.D.

EDWIN H. DWIGHT, *Director, Museum of Art, Munson, Williams, Proctor Institute* —E.H.D.

LEONARD B. DWORSKY, *Department of Health, Education and Welfare, Public Health Service* —L.B.D.

THOMAS EBERHARD, *Forest Ranger, Colorado* —T.E.

DON R. ECKLEBERRY, *Artist, Author* —D.E.

BRAYTON EDDY, *Formerly, Curator of Insects, The New York Zoological Society* —B.E.

J. GORDON EDWARDS, *Associate Professor of Entomology, San Jose State College* —J.G.E.

NELL B. ELDER, *Writer* —N.B.E.

PAUL L. ERRINGTON, *Ecologist* —P.L.E.

HOWARD E. EVANS, *Associate Curator of Insects, Museum of Comparative Zoology, Harvard University* —H.E.

NELL WOMACK EVANS —N.W.E.

DAVID and SUE FABLES, *Nature writers* —D.F. and S.F.

HARRIETT FARNSWORTH —H.F.

WALTER W. FERGUSON, *Bird Artist and Author* —W.W.F.

RICHARD B. FISCHER, *Professor of Rural Education, Cornell University* —R.B.F.

JAMES FISHER, *Ornithologist and Author* —J.F.

FRANK F. GANDER, *Ornithologist and Nurseryman* —F.G.

DOROTHY GARDINER, *Author* —D.G.

WEBB B. GARRISON, *Author* —W.B.G.

MARIE E. GAUDETTE, *Nature Adviser* —M.E.G.

WILLIS J. GERTSCH, *Curator, Department of Insects and Spiders, The American Museum of Natural History* —W.J.G.

GEORGE G. GOODWIN, *Curator Emeritus, Department of Mammals, The American Museum of Natural History* —G.G.G.

ROBERT B. GORDON —R.B.G.

ARTHUR HARMOUNT GRAVES, *Botanist* —A.H.G.

ALICE GRAY, *Specialist in Entomological Education; Scientific Assistant, Department of Entomology, American Museum of Natural History* —A.G.

HAROLD V. GREEN, *Author and Nature Photographer* —H.V.G.

WILLIAM C. GRIMM —W.C.G.

C. J. GUIGUET, *Former Director, Natural History Museum, Vancouver Island, British Columbia* —C.J.G.

DAVID GUNSTON, *Natural History writer* —Da.G.

HENRY MARION HALL, *Naturalist and Author* —H.M.H.

LOUIS J. HALLE, Jr., *Nature Writer* —L.J.H.,Jr.

WILLIAM F. HALLSTEAD —W.F.H.

WILLIAM J. HAMILTON, Jr., *Formerly Professor of Zoology, Cornell University; Mammalogist, Ecologist and Food Habits Investigator* —W.J.H.,Jr.

CHARLES A. HARWELL —C.A.H.

WILLIAM G. HASSLER, *Treasurer, Carolina Bird Club, Staff Member North Carolina State Museum* —W.G.H.

WELDON F. HEALD, *Freelance Writer* —W.H.

C. J. HENRY, *Formerly Manager of Souris Wildlife Refuge* —C.J.H.

EMMETT HERLOCKER —E.H.

RUTH LOUISE HINE —R.L.H.

STEPHEN W. HITCHCOCK, *Entomologist, Connecticut Agricultural Experiment Station* —S.W.H.

MARY HOLTZOFF —M.H.

HELEN HOOVER, *Nature Writer* —H.H.

ELIZABETH INGLES —E.I.

HARTLEY H. T. JACKSON, *Biologist, United States Fish and Wildlife Service (retired)* —H.H.J.

MORRIS K.JACOBSON, *Conchologist* —M.K.J.

HOPE SATTERTHWAITE JEX, *Author* —H.S.J.

GEORGE KARGER —G.K.

CHARLES A. KEMPER, M.D. —C.A.K.

KARL W. KENYON, *Biologist, United States Fish and Wildlife Service* —K.W.K.

RUTH KIRK —R.K.

H. W. KITCHEN, *Still and Motion Picture Producer* H.W.K.

ROBERT D. LEE —R.D.L.

JOSIAH L. LOWE, *Author* —J.L.L.

FRANK E. LUTZ, *Curator Emeritus of Entomology, The American Museum ofNatural History* —F.E.L.

YOLANDE LYON, *Consultant in Health Education, State of California, Department of Public Health* —Y.L.

ANNE MARIE MARK —A.M.M.

EDWIN A. MASON, *Director of the Acadia Wildlife Sanctuary, Northhampton-Easthampton, Massachusetts* —E.A.M.

ERNST MAYR, *Taxonomist and evolutionist, Harvard University* —E.M.

W. L. McATEE, *Wildlife Conservationist, Biologist, and Bird Food Habits Investigator for the United States Fish and Wildlife Service, formerly the Biological Survey* —W.L.M.

NEIL T. McMILLAN —N.T.M.

OLIVER P. MEDSGER, *Author* —O.P.M.

LORUS J. and MARGERY J. MILNE, *Department of Zoology, University of New Hampshire* —L.J.M. and M.J.M.

CHARLES E. MOHR, *Director Emeritus, Audubon Center, Greenwich, Connecticut* —C.E.M.

ANN H. MORGAN —A.H.M.

DURYEA MORTON, *Naturalist* —D.M.

JOHN T. NICHOLS, *Curator Emeritus of Fishes, The American Museum of Natural History* —J.T.N.

LOU WILLIAMS PAGE —L.W.P.

E. LAURENCE PALMER, *Professor Emeritus of Rural Education, Cornell University* —E.L.P.

T. GILBERT PEARSON, *Former President, National Audubon Society* —T.G.P.

JAMES N. PERKINS, *Writer, Editor, Publisher* —J.N.P.

GRACE A. PETERSON —G.A.P.

ROGER TORY PETERSON, *Artist, Naturalist, formerly on staff and member of Board of Directors of the National Audubon Society, Author,* A Field Guide to the Birds, *and others* —R.T.P.

OLIN SEWALL PETTINGILL, Jr., *Secretary and member of the Board of Directors, the National Audubon Society, Director, Laboratory of Ornithology, Cornell University* —O.S.P.,Jr.

RICHARD S. PHILLIPS —R.S.P.

GAYLE PICKWELL —Ga.P.

RUTHERFORD PLATT, *Nature photographer* —R.P.

JAMES W. POLING, *Writer* —J.P.

CLIFFORD H. POPE, *Herpetologist, Author* —C.P.

GEORGE PORTER, *Naturalist, Photographer* —G.P.

RICHARD H. POUGH, *Former Research Associate, The National Audubon Society, Ecologist* —R.H.P.

WILLIAM O. PRUITT, Jr., *Visiting Professor in the Department of Zoology, University of Oklahoma* —W.O.P.,Jr.

CHARLES W. QUAINTANCE —C.W.Q.

A. L. RAND, *Chief Zoologist, Chicago Natural History Museum* —A.L.R.

MICHAEL REED, *Nature Writer* —M.R.

WILLIAM B. ROBERTSON, Jr., *Biologist, Everglades National Park* —W.B.R.,Jr.

JOHN P. ROOD —J.P.R.

RONALD N. ROOD, *Natural History Research Editor, Grolier Information Service* —R.N.R.

JOHN B. ROUTIEN —J.B.R.

HESTER M. RUSK —H.M.R.

EDNA L. RUTH —E.L.R.

WILFORD E. SANDERSON —W.E.S.

HUGO H. SCHRODER —H.H.S.

PAUL B. SEARS, *Honorary President, National Audubon Society* —P.B.S.

CHARLES and ELIZABETH SCHWARTZ, *Biologists, Conservation Commission of Missouri* —C.S. and E.S.

HERBERT F. SCHWARZ, *Research Associate, Department of Insects and Spiders, The American Museum of Natural History* —H.F.S.

ELLEN E. SHAW —E.E.S.

JOSEPH J. SHOMON, *Director of Nature Centers Division, National Audubon Society* —J.J.S.

CARL N. SHUSTER, Jr., *Marine Biologist, Instructor in Zoology, Rutgers University* —C.N.S.,Jr.

DOROTHY EDWARDS SHUTTLESWORTH, *Formerly Editor of Junior Natural History Magazine, The American Museum of Natural History* —D.E.S.

ALLEN G. SMITH, *Research Biologist, Denver Wildlife Research Center, Bureau of Sport Fisheries and Wildlife, United States Fish and Wildlife Service* —A.G.S.

IDA SMITH —I.S.

ROBERT SNEDIGAR, *Formerly Curator of Reptiles and Amphibians, Chicago Zoo* R.S.

LYLE K. SOWLS, *Biologist, United States Fish and Wildlife Service* —L.K.S.

HUGH SPENSER —H.S.

WALTER SPOFFORD, *Professor of Anatomy, Syracuse University* —W.S.

ALEXANDER SPRUNT, Jr., *Ornithologist* —A.S.,Jr.

ALEXANDER SPRUNT, IV, *Biologist* —A.S.,IV

WILLIAM B. STAPP, *Instructor, Allwood Audubon Center* —W.B.S.

J. A. STEIGER —J.A.S.

GEORGE B. STEVENSON —G.B.S.

PAUL A. STEWART, *Biologist, United States Fish and Wildlife Service* —P.A.S.

JOHN H. STORER, *Formerly President The Florida Audubon Society; Naturalist* —J.H.S.

LLOYD W. SWIFT, *Formerly, Chief, Division of Wildlife Management, United States Forest Service* —L.W.S.

JEFF SWINEBROAD, M.D., *Department of Botany and Zoology, Douglas College, Rutgers University* —J.S.

EDWIN WAY TEALE, *Naturalist, Author of* North with the Spring, Journey into Summer, *and others* —E.W.T.

ALLAN D. TELFORD, *Assistant Entomologist, Department of Biological Control, University of California at Berkeley* —A.D.T.

JOHN K. TERRES, *Naturalist, Editor, Biologist, Author,* Songbirds in Your Garden *and* The Wonders I See; *Editor,* Audubon Book of True Nature Stories, Discovery, *and other books; Compiler,* An Encyclopedia of North American Birds —J.K.T.

JOHN W. THOMSON, Jr., *Associate Professor of Botany, The University of Wisconsin* —J.W.T.

FRANK A. TINKER, *Freelance Writer* —F.A.T.

JESSIE HOWARD TOLLISON —J.H.T.

KATHERINE TOTTENHAM —K.T.

DOROTHY A. TREAT, *Naturalist and Teacher* —D.A.T.

V.W.TURBIVILLE —V.W.T.

JOE VAN WORMER, *Nature Photographer, Naturalist and Author* —J.V.W.

WILLIAM GOULD VINAL, *Author* —W.G.V.

HAROLD E. VOKES, *Geologist and Paleontologist, Tulane University* —H.E.V.

LEWIS WAYNE WALKER, *Museum biologist, Sonora Desert Museum* —L.W.W.

ROBERT BRUCE WHITE —R.B.W.

FARIDA A. WILEY, *Honorary Associate in Natural Science Education, The American Museum of Natural History* —F.A.W.

CONRAD L. WIRTH, *Formerly Director, United States National Park Service* —C.W.

ROGER P. WODEHOUSE, M.D. —R.P.W.

ROBERT S. WOODS —R.S.W.

WELDON D. WOODSON —W.D.W.

CAROL H. WOODWARD, *Nature Writer* —C.H.W.

NORMAN G. WOOLSEY —N.G.W.

ARTHUR B. WILLIAMS, *Ecologist, Cleveland Museum of Natural History* —A.B.W.

FOREWORD

In bringing to you this new, significant, and lasting AUDUBON NATURE ENCYCLOPEDIA, which draws from the accumulated resources of our many years of experience and activity in the natural resources conservation field, we of the National Audubon Society have an objective. We feel that millions of Americans are hungering for a new source of contact with the realities of their earthly environment, of the world of nature.

For nearly two thousand years man's exciting, halting struggle to become civilized has, ironically perhaps, actually divorced him from nature. And yet we are part of nature, dependent upon the fruits of the earth for our health and welfare, molded by the environment which we also mold. Today science is beginning to document, all over again, that man is of the dust, that he is indeed his brother's keeper, and that this brotherhood includes all God's creatures. In rising to the challenge of this broader awareness we will have to rethink the directions in which we want our civilization to move. We believe that it is only by enlarging his sympathies that man becomes truly civilized.

It is our hope that through this well-rounded work you will be better able to appreciate the broad scope of the National Audubon Society's purposes. We learned, long ago, that birds and other living things cannot be preserved for man's benefit and enjoyment unless the habitat they need is also preserved. Man's powerful new tools, when used unwisely, can be destructive. Today's conservation problems therefore include decisions concerning priorities in our uses of the land. Remember that these decisions are made at all levels—personal, corporate, and governmental.

Believing in the wisdom of nature's design, we devote our efforts and our modest resources to awakening the American people to the magnificence and the vital importance of their natural resources heritage. Because we are a nonprofit, public service membership organization, every penny of return to the National Audubon Society from this venture will be reinvested in conservation action and conservation education.

It is, then, to answer your question, "What enrichment, what peace of mind can I find in coming to know the things of this earth, which is my home?" that we have joined in this publishing venture. It is our hope that a journey through these pages will be a source of inspiration to you and your family to *personally* share in the preservation of the resources that have made this earth productive.

Carl W. Buchheister

Carl W. Buchheister, President
National Audubon Society

EDITOR'S INTRODUCTION

Throughout the centuries, poets, philosophers, artists, and scientists have struggled to describe nature—the greatest creation known to man. Perhaps none has more powerfully and purely expressed its glories than the immortal Dante who wrote that "Nature is the art of God."

To explain the origin of life and of nature is a task man will probably never accomplish to his satisfaction. For many of us, it is sufficient that nature exists. No man-made work of the brush, pen, or melody will ever match the rhythm, the beauty, the power to exalt and to awe that are uniquely nature's—the wild plunge of an osprey for a fish in a lake; the glow of a firefly in the summer dusk; the brilliance of hummingbirds at wild flowers in spring; the graceful arc of a leaping deer; the majesty of the largest living things on earth, the giant sequoia trees of California.

The artistry of nature has given us keen pleasure and inspiration from the beginning of our recorded history. But an *understanding* of the ways that nature works her miracles—the flight of a bird; the hibernation of a bat; the art of a spider spinning her silk; the navigation of animals by the stars and sun; the behavior of animals, and their strange and fascinating interrelationships with the plant and animal world—has been discovered by man only within the last few hundred years.

In providing you and your children with a part of this accumulated knowledge, illustrated with brilliant color photographs of animals and plants in their natural world, we are offering you the glories of a pageant filled with the drama and meaning of all life. To show you what man, the artist, has seen in nature, we have reproduced in full color many of the paintings from the elephant folio edition of that earliest and greatest American bird artist, John James Audubon, for whom the Audubon Society was named.

When I was very young, the word *Encyclopedia* was to me an awesome one. I went to the books with a respect for the power of the knowledge they offered—for knowledge is power—and with hunger for their facts. But I learned that I would not find in them the excitement of my favorite books of nature written early in this century by William Beebe, Ernest Thompson Seton, John Burroughs, and other American naturalists. In THE AUDUBON NATURE ENCYCLOPEDIA, I think you will have a pleasant surprise. Here you will find that the tradition of exciting early American nature writing has been carried on to the present day.

Written for all—adults and young—these books are different from the ordinary encyclopedia. Although its volumes are a ready reference of stimulating facts about nature, they are spiced with accounts, written by famous American naturalists, that have warmth and charm in the telling.

The factual items about birds, mammals, insects, trees, fishes, and wild flowers are interspersed with Roger Tory Peterson's stories of biomes, water, and grasslands, and Rachel Carson's revelations about the destructiveness of pesticides. The story of reptiles and amphibians has been written by the authority Charles M. Bogert of the American Museum of Natural History; of wolves and foxes, by one of his colleagues Edwin H. Colbert; how mammals are classified, by T. Donald Carter, former explorer and world-known mammalogist.

There are articles about the weather, the singing of thrushes, the care of small animal pets, attracting birds to the garden, how to make and stock a home aquarium, and the drama of animal life at a water hole and at a pond.

You can travel with Edwin Way Teale, noted American nature writer, on his youthful adventures in nature exploring; with Alan Devoe into the small, warm, and sometimes frightening world of the chipmunk. Wherever you go in these books, I think you will be enthralled, whether it is by the account of moose in Canada, bears in the United States, monkeys in Central America, or the wonderful and sometimes pathetic travels of birds in their mysterious migrations from the Arctic to South America.

The subjects in the volumes (A to Z) will be easy to find and a convenient cross-referencing system will guide you to the additional categories under which each subject is treated. The last volume includes a complete index to the subject matter in all the volumes. To use the books for their fullest value, follow the suggested reading references for more detailed or additional facts about each subject.

In the more than one thousand accounts written for THE AUDUBON NATURE ENCYCLOPEDIA one has the advantage of the best authorities. Authority is the basis on which any book of facts is built. Although the 200 or more contributing authors are themselves authorities on the subjects they have written about, they and the editor must rely on books that are recognized as one, or sometimes more than one, authority in each field or branch of nature. Following are a few of the hundreds of authorities we have consulted in writing and assembling THE AUDUBON NATURE ENCYCLOPEDIA.

Birds

Check-List of North American Birds—Compiled by The American Ornithologists' Union. 1957 Edition.
Check-List of Birds of the World—James Lee Peters. A multivolume series.
Handbook of North American Birds—Ralph S. Palmer.
The Auk—Official publication of The American Ornithologists' Union.

Mammals

List of North American Recent Mammals—Gerrit S. Miller, Jr. and Remington Kellogg.
The Mammals of North America—E. Raymond Hall and Keith R. Kelson (Two Volumes).
The Journal of Mammalogy—Official publication of The American Society of Mammalogists.

Reptiles and Amphibians

A Field Guide to the Reptiles and Amphibians—Roger Conant.
The Natural History of North American Amphibians and Reptiles—James Oliver.
Copeia—Official journal of the American Society of Ichthyologists and Herpetologists.

Fishes

Freshwater Fishes of the World—Gunther Sterba.
Field Book of Marine Fishes of the Atlantic Coast—Charles M. Breder, Jr.
Field Book of Fresh-water Fishes of North America—Ray Schrenkiesen.
Copeia—Official journal of the American Society of Ichthyologists and Herpetologists.

Insects

Introduction to Entomology—J. H. Comstock.
College Entomology—E. O. Essig.
Field Book of Insects—Frank Lutz.
Annals of the Entomological Society of America.

Invertebrates in General

The Invertebrates—Libbie Hyman. A multivolume series.
Animals without Backbones—Ralph Buchsbaum.
Field Book of Seashore Life—Roy Waldo Miner.

Plants

Gray's Manual of Botany (Eighth Edition).
Illustrated Flora of the Northeastern United States and Adjacent Canada—Britten and Brown (Three Volumes).
Flora of the Rocky Mountains and Plains—P. A. Rydberg.
An Illustrated Flora of the Pacific States—Leroy Abrams (Four Volumes).
Manual of Cultivated Plants—Liberty Hyde Bailey.
Manual of Cultivated Trees and Shrubs—Alfred Rehder.

A complete list of the references used in the production of THE AUDUBON NATURE ENCYCLOPEDIA is published in the bibliography at the end of the last volume.

John K. Terres

John K. Terres,
EDITOR-IN-CHIEF

PICTORIAL ACKNOWLEDGMENTS, Volume 1

Paul Favour, XVI —Allan Brooks, 2, 3, 4, 75, 80, 147 —John H. Gerard*, 5 top, 55, 64 bottom left, 67 —Harry L. and Ruth Crockett*, 5 center —Allan D. Cruickshank*, 5 bottom, 8 27 bottom, 28 top, 64 top left, 64 center left, 64 bottom right, 66, 112, 148 —Walter Ferguson, 6, 7 —G. Ronald Austing, 9, 24, 82 —Eric Hosking*, 10 top —Roger Tory Peterson*, 10 center —Donald M. Cooper*, 10 bottom —Walter Dawn*, 11 —Harry Brevoort*, 13 —Los Angeles County Air Pollution Control District, 15 top —California State Department of Public Health, Graphic Arts Division, 15 bottom —University of California at Los Angeles, 16 —University of California at Riverside, 17 —Karl W. Kenyon*, 21 —Alfred M. Bailey*, 23, 122, 162 —Charles E. Mohr*, 25 top left, 93, 157 —Richard C. Finke*, 25 top right —Karl H. Maslowski* and Woodrow Goodpaster*, 25 bottom —G. Blake Johnson*, 26 —G. J. McWilliams*, 29 -George Porter, 31, 39, 42, 47, 49, 51, 52, 53, 56, top and center, 133, 146 —SuZan N Swain, 32, 40, 108 —Hugh Spencer*, 33, 184 —Stephen Collins*, 34 —Clifford Matteson*, 37 —Robert Hermes*, 45 —Lynwood M. Chace*, 54, 97, 99 top, 100 bottom —Gordon S. Smith*, 56 bottom, 74 —Karl H. Maslowski, 57, 77 —Lee Adams, 58, 59, 127, 132 —Bucky Reeves*, 60 —A. W. Ambler*, 61, 169 left —Jeff Swinebroad, 63 —Edward F. Dana*, 64 top right —Leonard Lee Rue*, 68 —Betty Barford*, 69 top —Charles J. Ott*, 69 bottom, 120-121 —Ellsworth Jaeger, 70-71 —Jack Dermid*, 73 —R. Van Nostrand*, 76, 165 bottom —Hal H. Harrison*, 79, 158 —United States Department of Agriculture, 86, 190 —Robert Seibert, 87 —Matthew Kalemanoff, 91 —W. Treat Davidson*, 94, 109 top, 110, 174, 176, 181, 183 bottom —William J. Jahoda*, 96, 186—Shirley Howard, 99 bottom, 100 —Bernard L. Gluck*, 105 top —A. G. Wright, 105 bottom —Fran Hall*, 106 —New York Zoological Gardens, 107 —General Biological Supply House, Inc., 109 bottom —Jeanne White*, 111 top —Drawings from "A Naturalist in the Great Lakes", 11 bottom —Ernst Peterson, 114, 117 —Robert Jackowitz, 118, 151, 164, 167 —Gale Pickwell*, 119, 124 —Bruce Horsfall, 123 —W.D. Berry, 125, 150, 159, 171 —Woodrow Goodpaster*, 156 —W. J. Schoonmaker*, 165 top —W. Gillett*, 169 right —Helen Cruickshank*, 173 —Ralph J. and Mildred L. Donahue*, 179 —Donald J. Borror, 182, 183 top —Hiram Parent*, 192

* Photographs from Photo-Film Service of National Audubon Society

The rocky coast of Acadia National Park, Maine

ACADIA NATIONAL PARK

Location—Mount Desert Island, Maine
Size—42 square miles
Mammals—Beavers, deer, chipmunks, red squirrels
Birdlife—Bald eagles, ospreys, loons, great blue herons, cormorants, gulls; in summer, thrushes, warblers, and other songbirds.
Plants—Spruces, pines, firs, hemlocks, beeches, birches, maples, mosses, and lichens; cardinal flowers, pitcherplants, lady's slippers

Footpaths lead the visitor to all parts of the park, along the rocky cliffs overlooking the ocean, over pebble beaches, up ladder trails to barren peaks, through deep conifer forests. Naturalists and rangers conduct tours and lectures on all aspects of the park.
Accommodations—Two campgrounds in the park, summer hotels in Ellsworth and Bar Harbor
Headquarters—Bar Harbor, Maine

ACCIPITERS

The Short-winged Hawks

These are birds of swift pursuit, with short rounded wings and long tails. They are capable of quick maneuvers and are masters of the art of dodging and dashing. The short-winged hawks are primarily birds of the woods and can move through the network of branches with amazing dexterity and speed.

These birds are often called the *blue darters* as the adults are a blue-gray color and appear and disappear with such rapidity. They are the bird hawks—the goshawk, Cooper's hawk, and sharp-shinned hawk—and are experts at keeping out of sight. They seldom soar but alternately flap and glide when in the open. For the most part they stay well hidden in the leafy part of a tree except when engaged in actual pursuit of their prey. The sharp-shinned, smallest of the trio, preys on small birds. The other two take larger birds as well—chickens too when readily accessible.

The flight pattern of bird hawks

However, these birds are not the blackguards they may seem. Although song birds and gamebirds are not as prolific as mice, they could, even with their annual reproduction of one or two broods, quickly overpopulate an area. Overpopulation may cause starvation and disease. These short-winged, long-

Allan Brooks

tailed accipiters are among nature's controls, keeping the population of birds and other animals in check, and healthy too, for it is the less alert and the slow that naturally are the first to fall prey to the bird hawks. They play a valuable role in any wildlife community in maintaining a healthy balance between food supply and population. Shooting a Cooper's hawk and goshawk is not the way to increase gamebirds. Gamebirds are best protected by improving their environment. Chickens can best be protected by raising them under wire. The value of even the bird hawk is now recognized in many states where, along with the mouse hawks and falcons, they are protected by law from indiscriminate shooting. (*See also under Hawk*) —D.A.T.

Cooper's Hawk
Other Common Names—Pigeon hawk, chicken hawk, blue darter
Scientific Name—*Accipiter cooperii*
Family—Accipitridae (hawks, Old World vultures, and harriers)
Order—Falconiformes
Size—Length, 14 to 20 inches
Range—Breeds in southern Canada and most of the United States; winters in the United States

Cooper's hawk is smaller, slimmer and with a smaller head than the goshawk. It is usually larger than the sharp-shinned hawk, but the sizes intergrade, and a large female sharp-shinned hawk may be as big as a small, male Cooper's. The best feature for separating these birds is the tail. In Cooper's, the tail is rounded, and in the sharp-shinned hawk it is square at the tip and notched.

Goshawk
Other Common Names—Hen hawk, dove hawk
Scientific Name—*Accipiter gentilis*
Family—Accipitridae (hawks, Old World vultures, and harriers)
Order—Falconiformes
Size—Length, 20 to 26 inches
Range—Breeds in wooded regions in central Alaska and Canada south to northern New England and mountains of central California; winters to Virginia, Missouri, and New Mexico

The goshawk is the largest of the three accipiters, all of which share the silhouette of short, rounded wings and long tails, and the flight habit of alternating a burst of powerful wingbeats with a short glide. The adult is light gray below, where other accipiters have rusty stripes. The young of all three varieties are much alike, but the young goshawk has a more prominent white stripe over the eyes, is larger, and has a proportionately bigger head. —G.B.S.

Cooper's hawk

Goshawks, adult (left); immature (right)

Sharp-shinned hawks

Sharp-shinned Hawk
Other Common Names—Sparrow hawk (European name), little blue darter
Scientific Name—*Accipiter striatus*
Family—Accipitridae (hawks, Old World vultures, and harriers)
Order—Falconiformes
Size—Length, 10 to 14 inches
Range—Breeds from treeline in Canada to Gulf of Mexico to Arizona; winters in the United States

The sharp-shinned hawk is the smallest of the three accipiters. Unlike the others, the tail in this species appears notched when folded, and square-cut when the bird is in flight. Its prey consists largely of the smaller birds, those of sparrow size. —G.B.S.

ADAPTATIONS OF BIRDS

Every living organism is definitely adjusted for existence in a certain kind of habitat. Among birds there are hundreds of modifications of structure fitting them for life in the varied regions of the world. These adaptations serve as aids in nest building, protection from predators, and tools for food-getting. All such attributes are important for the survival of each species in its natural environment. (*See also under Bird*)

Bird Vision

Most birds have extremely keen vision. One pair of eyes may combine both telescopic and microscopic ability. Hawks, eagles, and vultures, particularly, benefit by being able to sight their food at great distances. Good eyesight plus rapid focusing are a great help to birds that pursue their prey. An extra, transparent eyelid, the nictitating membrane, serves as goggles to keep the eye clean, reduce glare, and prevent excessive watering which rapid passage through the air might induce. The membrane also protects the eyes of diving birds and underwater swimmers.

One reason for such good vision is the relatively large size of a bird's eyes, each eye often being as large as the bird's brain. It is said that if human eyes were proportionately as big, each eye would weigh about five pounds. Besides exceptional eyes, birds have many other features to help them "earn their living," build a home for the family, and procure food. Modifications of bills, tongues, tails, wings, feet, shape of body, all play important parts in the lives of birds.

Woodpecker Adaptations

The strong, straight bill of the woodpecker, and the hammerlike action of its head are familiar to many, but the horny-tipped tongue, supplied with barbs and with muscles for extending the tongue with force into the chiseled holes, is the tool that captures the insect under the bark. The brushlike tongue of the sapsucker (also a woodpecker) lacks the horny tip but fills with sap as a paintbrush fills with paint. It also serves as a tiny broom to sweep in the insects attracted by the flowing sap. The flicker, a woodpecker whose diet is chiefly ants obtained from the ground, has only one barb on its horny-tipped tongue.

However, the woodpecker's hammer could not function if the bird were not firmly anchored to the tree trunk. This is accomplished in two ways. A woodpecker has its toes divided, two forward and two backward, enabling them to grip the bark like tongs. Furthermore, the tail feathers are pointed, with the tip of the shaft protruding, thus making the tail a good prop when the bird is clinging to the trunk or limb of a tree.

More Tail Props

Not only woodpeckers use their tails as props. There is also the brown creeper that hops slowly up the tree trunk as it probes crevices in the bark for food. Chimney swifts also use their tails for props, an extremely important matter for these fliers that apparently never come to rest except against a vertical wall inside a hollow tree or chimney. It is in this position that the swift builds its nest, gluing the sticks to each other and to the wall by means of its saliva which dries to form a kind of cement—another special adaptation of bird life.

Feet That Lock

Many persons wonder how robins, sparrows, blackbirds and other common species can perch on a small branch and go to sleep without falling off, even if rocked severely by the wind. The sleeping bird is actually "locked" on the branch. When the bird relaxes in sleep, its body slumps down on its feet. In this position, a tendon passing behind

Perching birds, such as this starling, have feet that lock when they relax

The Gila woodpecker, a climbing bird, grips trees with ice-tonglike feet

Swimming birds, like ducks, have fully webbed feet that they use as paddles

the heel is pulled tight. This draws the three forward toes and the hind toe toward each other, clamping the bird on the twig. When the bird rises to a standing position a second tendon releases the clamp. The tendons are easily found and operated in the feet of a freshly killed chicken.

Bird Bills

Most adaptations of birds are connected with getting food. There are the strong curved talons of the hawks and owls for grasping prey and their hooked

Adaptations of BILLS

SEED-EATING—(a) short, thick bill for crushing seeds. *Examples:* Sparrow, Grosbeak, Bunting,—Finch *(shown)*
(b) upper and lower mandibles crossed to enable bird to extract seeds from cones of evergreen trees. *Example:* Crossbill *(shown)*

INSECT-EATING — (a) slender, pointed beak for picking up insects. *Examples:* Warbler,—Vireo *(shown)*
(b) very wide mouth for catching insects on the wing. *Examples:* Swallow, Nighthawk, Swift

PROBING—(a) long, slender bill for probing in mud in search of food. *Examples:* Snipe *(shown)*, Woodcock, other Sandpipers
(b) long, slender bill for probing the necks of flowers to feed on nectar. *Example:* Hummingbird

PREYING—strong, sharp, hooked bill for tearing flesh of prey. *Examples:* Owl, Hawk, — Falcon *(shown)*

Adaptations of WINGS

Long, pointed wings for fast, easy flight in the pursuit of flying insects. *Examples:* Swallow,—Swift *(shown)*

Long, broad wings for strong, soaring, effortless flight. *Examples:* Hawk *(shown)*, Eagle

Short, rounded wings for speedy take-off and fast flight over comparatively short distances. *Examples:* Sparrow, Quail,—Pheasant *(shown)*, Woodcock, Grouse

Adaptations of FEET

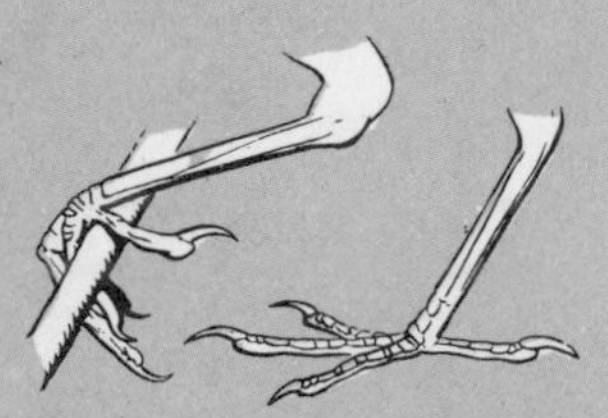

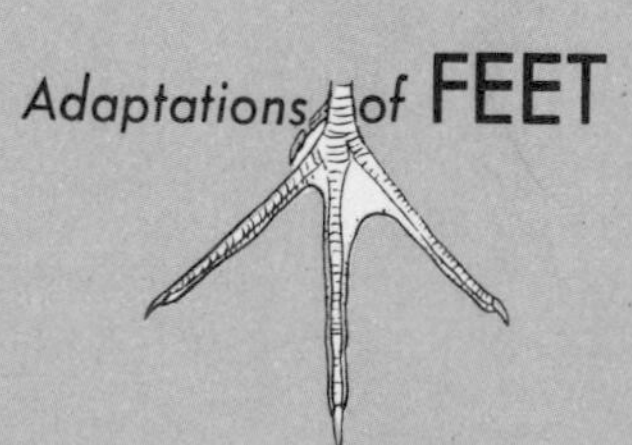

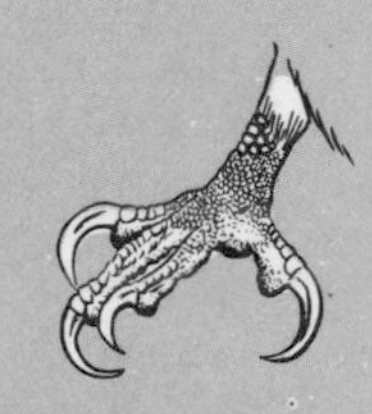

PERCHING—three toes in front, one toe behind. Most familiar birds are of this type. The foot automatically clasps the perch when the leg is relaxed. *Examples:* Sparrow, Chickadee,—Robin *(shown)*

WADING—long legs, long, slender toes. The three long toes keep bird from sinking into the mud. *Examples:* Gallinule, Heron,—Sandpiper *(shown)*

PREYING—powerful feet and legs with strong, curved, sharp talons for grasping prey. *Examples:* Hawk, Owl,—Eagle *(shown)*

beaks for tearing flesh. There are literally hundreds of modifications of bills that especially fit birds for obtaining a definite type of food. A good example of a highly specialized bill is that of the crossbills whose mandibles cross over, a very convenient arrangement for prying off the scales of pine and spruce cones to reach the seeds at the base of the scales. Parrots have a similar beak for tearing fruit apart (*See also under Bird*).

Most ducks, geese and swans have wide scooplike bills with which they can shovel up submerged plant and animal food. The water is forced out through the sievelike edges of the bill while the food is retained. The fish-eating merganser ducks have narrow bills with sharp serrations along the margins which must be quite an aid in hanging onto slippery fishes.

Many insects live and lay their eggs in bark crevices or among the leaves. The slender bills of warblers, chickadees, titmice, nuthatches, and creepers are adapted for getting at these foods and picking them up.

STRAINING—broad, flattened bill for straining food from mud. *Examples:* Flamingo, Duck,—Goose *(shown)*

GROUND-FEEDING—short, stout bill for feeding on the ground, as a hen. *Example:* Bob-White *(shown)*

FISH-EATING—(a) long and sharp for spearing fish. *Example:* Heron *(shown)*

(b) with a flexible pouch underneath bill for holding captured fish. *Example:* Pelican *(shown)*

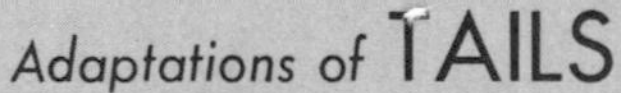

Adaptations of TAILS

Tail feathers with strong, spine-like tips for use as a prop or support when clinging to vertical surfaces. *Examples:* Woodpecker, Swift,—Brown Creeper *(shown)*

Broad, fanned tail for soaring. *Example:* Buteo-type Hawk *(shown)*

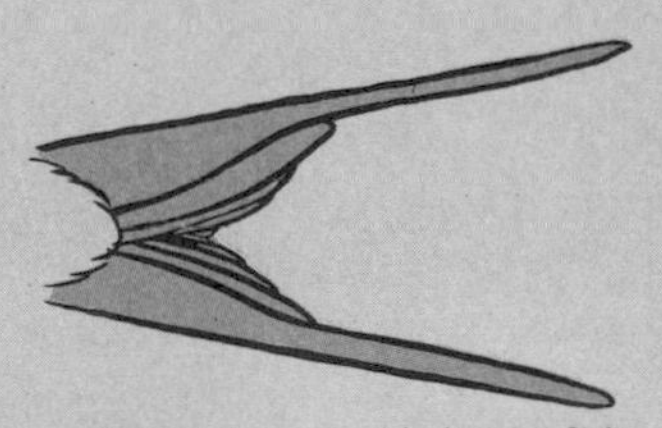

Long, forked tail for graceful, skimming flight and extreme maneuverability. *Examples:* Tern, —Barn Swallow *(shown)*, Frigate Bird, Swallow-Tailed Kite

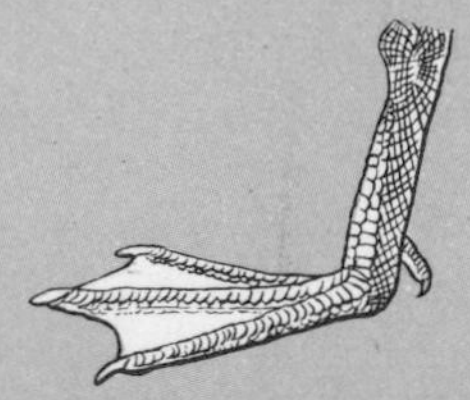

SWIMMING—three front toes fully webbed. *Examples:* Goose, Gull,—Duck *(shown)*

CLIMBING—two toes in front, two toes in back; sharp claws for clinging to an upright surface with ease. *Example:* Woodpecker *(shown)*

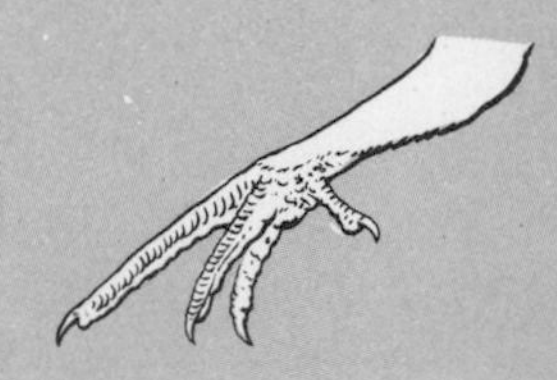

SCRATCHING — claws strong and blunt for raking or scratching the ground for food, as a hen. *Examples:* Pheasant, Quail,—Grouse *(shown)*

Plant seeds of assorted sizes are the main food of sparrows, finches, grosbeaks, cardinals, and others, especially in cold weather. All of these birds are equipped with relatively short but stout bills, useful in removing the hard seed coat to expose the tender kernel. At the same time, the sharp tips of the bill enable the birds to vary their diet in warmer weather by capturing insects.

Long Legs, Necks, and Toes for Feeding in Shallow Water

Each depth of water along ponds, lakes, and oceans has its group of the feeding bird population. Long-legged ibises, cranes, egrets, bitterns, and other species of herons wade into water a foot or more deep to catch their aquatic food. Their long legs terminate in feet with very long toes which help to distribute the weight to keep these birds from sinking too deeply into the mud or sand of the shores. They have long necks to compensate for the length of their legs; otherwise they would be unable to catch the fish, the crayfish or other swimming or stationary food in the water beneath them. The "comb" on the toe of the heron tribe is a convenient tool for preening (straightening out) the feathers. Most birds depend wholly on the bill for preening.

The long, slender toes of the common egret, a wading bird, keep it from sinking too deeply into the mud of swamps

In waters only a few inches deep, many of the shorebirds such as sandpipers, plovers, snipe, and others, feed on animals that live in the soft muds or sands of shores. Many of these birds have rather long bills with which they probe for food. Along the ocean some sandpipers scurry out with the retreating waves to pick up food that is exposed and then hurry in just ahead of the next incoming wave, keeping just ahead of the water.

Underwater Feeders

For birds that find the deeper waters a rich feeding territory, webbed feet usually furnish the propellers for locomotion beneath the water. Some few birds, such as the puffins and murres and cormorants, make use of their wings to propel themselves when fishing for their aquatic food. Diving birds have beautifully streamlined bodies with the legs set near the rear of the body. As a result they have to stand more erectly than do landbirds. This overweight of the body in front makes them very awkward on land. Such diving birds as the grebe or loon nest in or at the edge of water so they can slip directly into it without having to walk over land. Birds such as gannets, murres, puffins, and the like commonly nest on cliffs from which they can launch themselves into the air.

Some Wing Modifications

The many shapes and sizes of wings that make it possible for birds to feed and nest in different types of habitats is, of course, important to their survival. Birds that nest and feed in grass-covered or brush-covered areas must be able to fly almost vertically from the ground. Strong legs and feet coupled with short wings enable them to do this. The strong legs and feet are

Brushland birds, such as this bobwhite, have short wings for vertical take-offs

used to catapult them into the air and the short wings do not become entangled with plant growth. Among birds so equipped are meadowlarks, quail, pheasants and sparrows. Birds that nest and feed among shrubs or among the branches of trees also tend to have short wings.

Birds that must pursue their food in flight usually have long, narrow, and angled wings. Swallows, swifts, nighthawks, and whippoorwills all pursue flying insects. They have rather wide-gaping mouths also, a kind of flytrap. The flycatchers are another group of birds that catch flying insects but they have a different technique for doing so. They sit on a tree branch or other perch and wait for an insect to fly past, then dart out after it.

Vultures, eagles, and many of the hawks that search from the air for their food on the ground have broad wings that make it possible for them to soar on set wings when the air currents are right. A number of the broad-winged birds hover (hold themselves in one spot in the air) for a short time while they search the ground for any movement that might indicate the presence of insects or rodents upon which they feed. (*See also under Hawk*)

The broad-winged night-feeders, the owls, have "silencers" in the form of frayed margins of the feathers of the wings and tails. This means of silent flight is an efficient aid in catching rodents such as mice and rats, the principal food of most owls. (*See under Owl*)

Birds having extremely long or broad wings live in open areas. The wandering albatross, which possesses the widest sweep of wing of any bird in the world (11 feet 4 inches) spends all of its days over the oceans with the exception of the nesting period. (*See under Albatross*) During this time it occupies areas that provide long, flat expanses over which it can make a running start to get into the air. All of its food comes from the ocean. The Andean and California condors, which have the next largest wingspread, usu-

The crossed mandibles of the red cross-bill's bill are highly specialized for extracting the seeds from pine cones

Many waterbirds that are bottom feeders have scooplike bills with which they shovel up plant and animal matter

Birds of prey, such as this osprey have sharp, downcurved upper mandibles that are useful for tearing flesh

ally launch themselves from cliffs. (*See under Condor.*) The American bald eagle, with a wingspread of about seven feet, commonly frequents shores of lakes, large rivers, and seashores on its hunting expeditions. Thus it has wide open spaces in which to launch itself into the air. (*See Eagle*)

Hummingbird

This is a bird with amazing adaptations. Beating its wings 50 to 75 times per second, it can fly at great speed and hover. It can fly backward too, and can dart in and out of flowers. With its long bill and grooved tongue, it sips nectar from the tubes of even the most delicate and fragile blossoms.

Lightness

All birds have feathers, the warmest, lightest, strongest and most durable and flexible covering known, and *only* birds have feathers. Additional lightness is gained by air spaces within their bones. These are connected to the five pairs of air sacs distributed through the bird's body, another adaptation for lightness and the chief organ for respiration.

—F.A.W.

Recommended Reading

Biology and Comparative Physiology of Birds (two volumes)—Edited by A. J. Marshall. Academic Press, New York.

Bird—Lois and Louis Darling. Houghton Mifflin Company, New York.

Birds and Their Attributes—Glover M. Allen. Dover Publications, New York.

Book of Birdlife—Arthur A. Allen. D. Van Nostrand Company, Inc., New York.

Introduction to Ornithology—George J. Wallace. Macmillan, New York.

Living Birds of the World—E. Thomas Gilliard. Doubleday, New York.

Recent Studies in Avian Biology—Edited by Albert Wolfson, University of Illinois Press, Urbana.

The Birds—Oskar and Katharina Heinroth. University of Michigan Press, Ann Arbor.

The Life of Birds—Joel Carl Welty. W.B. Sanders Company, Philadelphia.

AEROBATICS (*See under Bird Flight*)

The paca, or spotted cavy, is a member of the agouti family

AGOUTI
Other Common Names—None
Scientific Name—*Dasyprocta punctata*
Family—Dasyproctidae (agoutis and pacas)
Order—Rodentia
Size—Body length, 20 to 25 inches; tail, 1 inch
Range—Southern Mexico, Central America, South America

The agouti is a nervous, delicately built, active mammal that is said to resemble an animal with a rabbit's head and a pig's body. Actually, it is a large, apparently tailless rodent that burrows into the ground along heavily forested ravines. A native name for the agouti is *nequi,* derived from its shrieking cries of *nequi! nequi! nequi!*

Although normally active during the day, the agoutis have been so persistently hunted that the much reduced population is now shy in most places and active only during the hours of dusk. Nowadays, most of their burrows are in cool woodlands, among boulders.

The agouti is a creature of remarkable habits. It can jump great distances and has been observed to leap 20 feet. It is even capable of ascending trees to eat fruit. The agouti is able to swim, and some have been seen grubbing about ocean shores eating shellfish. It eats sitting on its haunches and takes its food in its forepaws, displaying much finger dexterity despite its long claws.

There are really two different groups of agoutis. Ironically, their common names do not at all match the scientific names. Members of the genus *Agouti* are called pacas by mammalogists, whereas it is the members of the genus *Dasyprocta* that the scientist has tagged agouti.

M. H. BEVANS

AILANTHUS
Other Common Names—Tree of heaven, sumac
Scientific Name—*Ailanthus altissima*
Family—Polygalaceae (milkwort family)
Range—Native of China but widely planted and naturalized in eastern United States, southern Rocky Mountains, and Pacific states
Habitat—Grows rapidly in even the poor soils of city yards, around abandoned buildings, and often along railroad embankments
Leaves—Compound, usually 18 to 30 inches long (sometimes three feet or more) with 11 to 14 rather broad leaflets on a tapering, whiplike stem. Very large, hoof-shaped leaf scars
Bark—Generally smooth and gray (yellow-brown on twigs), becoming uniformly rough with age
Flowers—Large plumes (panicles) of greenish blossoms, high on the tree in late spring or early summer
Fruit—Masses of pink and yellow, winged seeds, that become brown as they ripen and fall

The yellow-green, frondlike, foliage of the ailanthus, arching gracefully from the ends of the branches, has a decidedly tropical appearance. Although it does occur on the equatorial lands of southern Asia and the Indies, it is referred to as a native of northern China and proves its hardiness through our own northeastern winters.

Many areas such as city backyards, vacant lots, and tawdry industrial neighborhoods would be lifeless-looking places indeed were it not for this tree that seems able to endure, and even flourish, on the most sterile ground that will not support even the hardier native species. Of course, this vitality shows better results under more favorable conditions. The tree is reported to reach a height of 100 feet with a trunk diameter of three feet or more, but this is well over the average dimensions. At almost any age the smooth trunk and widely spaced, upsloping branches with their terminal foliage masses are easily recognizable traits. The whole tree has an open, composed appearance free from tangled limbs and twigs. In fact, due to the brittle quality of the dead wood, such branches soon snap off and the ailanthus might therefore be called a "self-trimming" species.

Perhaps less desirable are the heavily "scented" blossoms of the male trees that bother some people with allergies, but the female specimens produce an abundance of attractively colored, winged seeds that look somewhat like the paper "caps" used in toy guns. These blow freely in the wind and will even take root in cracks in a brick wall, but, oddly enough, they do not often grow in established forest areas, and fortunately seldom compete with the native trees.

However, ailanthus, the tree of heaven, can be an agreeable addition to many landscapes and is valuable in hot weather for its pleasant dappled shade. Some people locally call these trees *sumacs* and mistakenly regard the foliage as poisonous — possibly confusing it with harmless, native sumacs like the staghorn, ***Rhus typhina***, or the toxic, ***Rhus vernix***. (*See also under Ash; Tree*) —M.H.B.

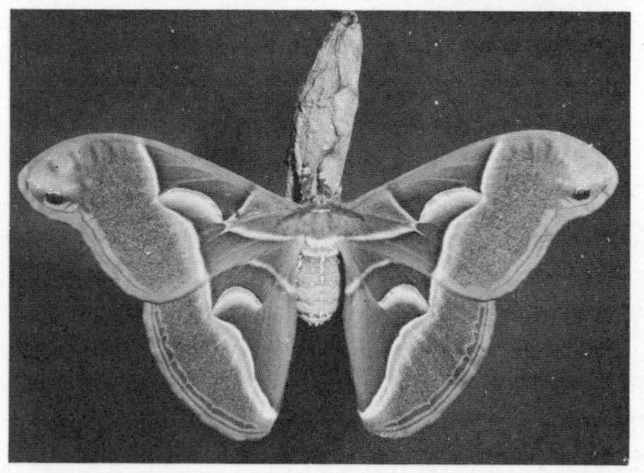

The ailanthus silk moth feeds largely on the leaves of the ailanthus tree

AIR PLANT (*See under Epiphyte*)

Ailanthus (above); staghorn sumac (below)

AIR POLLUTION

Air pollution can often be detected as a layer of gray or yellowish-brown haze on the horizon, known in some parts of the United States as *smog.* It is one of today's serious problems in conservation.

Although water pollution may remain a threat to public health in some areas, much progress has been made in combatting it. Communities have learned how to keep the water supply fit for use. Laws have been passed requiring the cooperation of entire communities, industries, and individuals in keeping the water supply free from pollution. It has also been learned how to process water before it reaches the consumer. Thus, water can be used with confidence as to its purity.

The air supply presents a similar problem, but little has been done so far to correct it. There is now a very unpleasant pollution of the air over most large cities, varying in degree and kind from place to place, depending on density of population and degree of industrialization. Most states and cities are beginning to recognize the problem and are searching for ways to cope with it. As always, some communities are slow to recognize that they do have this problem.

In its worst form, air pollution can cause disaster; in Los Angeles it causes an annoying eye irritation, producing discomfort to large numbers of people.

Air pollution is of concern because man lives in a sea of air and has very little choice about breathing anything harmful that may be in it. One can go several days without food or water but only a few moments without air. Treating the air supply in the same way as the water supply is not practical. Hence, the increasing pollution of the air is of concern to all. Seeing to it that the air is kept clean is part of conserving a very precious natural resource.

Air pollution casts a pall over the city. Favorite mountains and seascapes are hidden from view. Operational visibility for airplanes and automobiles is reduced. Buildings and clothing become soiled. In addition, eyes are irritated and plants are damaged by the types of air pollution experienced in California cities for more than 15 years and more recently in some areas of the East Coast.

The kind of air pollution referred to above is called *photochemical* air pollution. It is caused by a combination of dusts, droplets, gases, and chemicals that rise into the air and, when the sun shines upon them, react and interact to create an unpleasant haze. One may ask, "Why doesn't it blow away?" When there is good ventilation, the smog does go away. But if it occurs in an area which has slow winds, the air pollutants accumulate too fast to be dissipated. "Why, then, doesn't the air pollution disperse upward into the atmosphere?" The answer is that it usually does in most places. Normally, the air in the atmosphere above a city is cooler than the lower air. Being lighter, it is natural for warmer air to travel upward when the upper layer is cooler. At times, however, the upper atmosphere becomes warmer than the air below it. This condition is referred to as a *temperature inversion.* At such times the air of the city cannot disperse upward until the condition changes back to normal. Thus the air with all its pollutants lies stagnant over the city.

Temperature inversions in the valleys of the West Coast last throughout most of the day; the winds are often gentle and the sunshine plentiful. All three factors are favorable for photochemical air pollution. Temperature inversions occur in other parts of the United States, too, but they are less frequent and persist for only a few hours at a time.

Smoke and dust pollution, and pollution from single sources are found in all parts of the United States, sometimes even in rural areas. Community air pollution of the photochemical vari-

Many industries are controlling air pollution with electrostatic precipitation

ety is not so widespread but is being recognized as increasingly serious in cities of the United States and abroad. The difference between air pollution in Los Angeles and in some other large metropolitan areas with the same problems of urbanization is merely a matter of degree. Another difference may be the vigor with which each city has attacked its smog problem.

Sources of Pollutants

Where do the contaminants come from that pollute the air? The sources are many: smoke belching out of industrial stacks; clouds of smoke rising from open air dumps where refuse is being burned; smoke coming out of auto exhaust pipes, or from diesel buses and trucks. All of this smoke pollutes the air. In addition, these same sources emit pollutants that are invisible to the naked eye, and often the unseen pollutants are more troublesome than the visible ones.

Air pollution is a "disease" of urbanization. The more people there are in an area, the more there is need for industry, transportation, and disposal of refuse, and the more there is of pollution.

CLEAR DAY – NO INVERSION
SOME WIND

°F
50
55
60
65
70
Air cools gradually as height increases
3000 FT–
2000 FT–
1000 FT–
Ground level

On most days the lower air becomes warm by noon. It pushes upward through the progressively cooler air carrying air pollutants up and away

CLEAR DAY – INVERSION PRESENT
LITTLE WIND

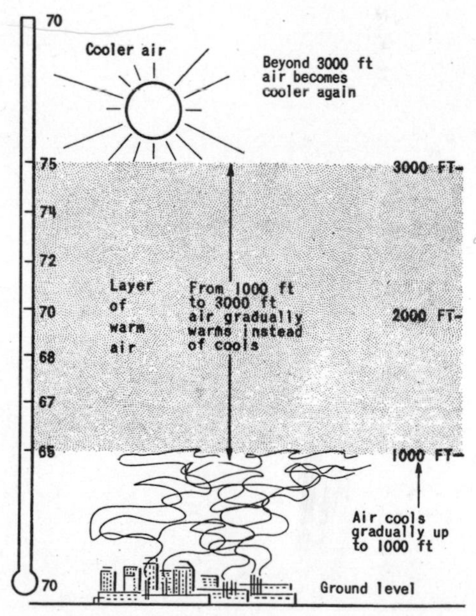

On days when a layer of warm air is present that has a ceiling below altitudes of 1,500 feet, air pollutants are unable to escape and remain suspended over cities

In another sense, air pollution results from the generation of heat and power. These are necessary for industrial processes, to make vehicles run, to burn useless materials to keep a community clean, and to keep homes warm. It might be concluded, therefore, that air pollution is unavoidable. This is not true. While all these forms of burning are necessary, air pollution is caused to a large extent because there is incomplete combustion, that is, incomplete burning. And combustion of all kinds *can* be improved.

In addition to the photochemical smog already described, there are plain smoke and dust problems. There are "point source" problems in which an otherwise unpolluted area will have a single major source of air pollution. Some examples are smoke from open fires, odors from processing plants, and dusts, fluorides, and sulfur dioxides from factories.

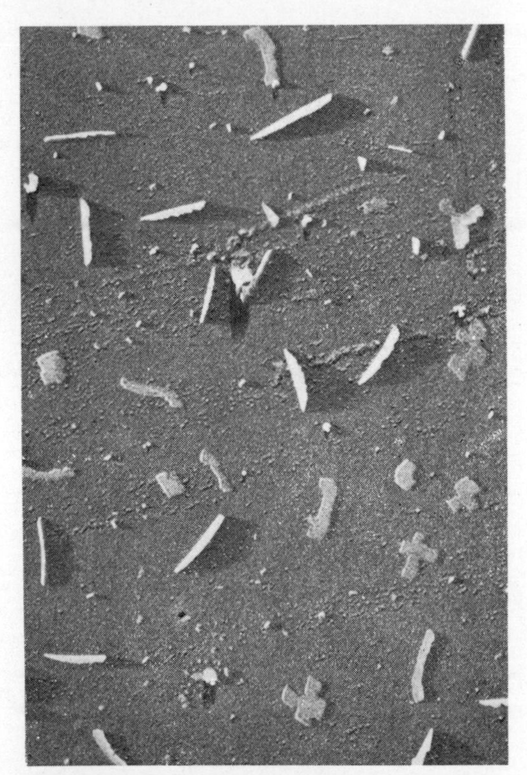

These unusual smog particles (magnified 18,000 times) were collected from the air at Los Angeles, California

As for specific pollutants, the best known are probably dust and smoke. Pittsburgh, Pennsylvania, and St. Louis, Missouri, suffered severely from these until people in the community decided to do something about it. Then there are sulfur dioxide, carbon monoxide, nitrogen dioxide, hydrogen sulfide, hydrocarbons, and many more. It is not necessary to go into the specifics of each of these pollutants except to say that many of them can be harmful to man, plants, or inanimate objects.

Air Pollution Disasters

How serious can air pollution get? Several episodes in the past provide an all too obvious answer. It is known that death may follow acute air pollution conditions. One such disaster occurred in the Meuse Valley of Belgium in 1930. This was an area in which were factories, coke ovens, blast furnaces, and steel mills, power plants; and a plant making fertilizer and sulfuric acid. Homes in the valley were heated by coal. The area had been blanketed by fog for three days and it can be assumed that ventilation was not adequate to disperse all the smoke and gases. Thousands of persons became ill and 60 died.

Another disaster occurred in Donora, Pennsylvania, also a heavy industrial area. This city is surrounded by high hills on four sides. One week in October 1948, Donora had fog, a temperature inversion, and low winds. Pollutants could not disperse either upward or horizontally. Close to 6,000 persons became ill and 20 died. With the return of normal weather the epidemic stopped.

Similar weather conditions prevailed in an air pollution episode in London, England. Again there was a great deal of illness and a rise in the number of deaths. Residents reported much discomfort, including eye irritation, cough, shortness of breath, and other unpleasant symptoms.

Effects on Health

Many air pollutants are generally known to be harmful or lethal in large quantities. It is well known, for instance, that carbon monoxide in high concentrations will cause death. It is not equally well known that, even in low concentrations, over a sufficiently long period of time, some pollutants may have a very harmful effect. For example, fluorides that are thrown into the atmosphere in gas or solid form by certain industrial processes are quite harmful in high concentrations. Even in low concentration, however, they accumulate in the leaves of plants and, as a result, the teeth of grazing animals may deteriorate so badly that they are unable to feed.

Much of the research into the medical aspects of air pollution is focused on predicting the long-range effects of small amounts of pollutants over a long period of time—for this may be the real problem in air pollution.

Already it is known that there is a strong relationship between the occurrence of respiratory diseases, such as bronchitis and emphysema, and long-time residence in areas where there is air pollution. A link between cancer and air pollution is also suspected, but enough is not known about it as yet.

Low but continuous concentrations of pollutants unfortunately cause a considerable amount of discomfort. This is no small matter. A survey made in California found a large number of people so sensitive to the discomfort of air pollution that they wanted to move or change jobs. Eye irritation, one of the marks of photochemical air pollution, is well known to residents of the Los Angeles area and more recently has been experienced in other cities, including Washington, D.C., and New York City. Understandably, it is the subject of considerable research.

One medical researcher found that the lung functioning of his patients with emphysema improved when they were taken out of smoggy air and placed in rooms with air which had been passed through charcoal filters. In another investigation, four different kinds of animals—hamsters, rats, guinea pigs, and dogs – were exposed to small amounts of ozone (one part per million) for six hours a day for a year. Marked damage to the airway lining cells were found in guinea pigs, less marked changes resulted in rats and hamsters. This study was of value because it showed that subtle changes may take place in the human body on repeated exposures to levels of ozone which are not much greater than the ozone levels found in some California communities.

The effects of air pollution on growing plants is a vital subject of research

It may come as a surprise to readers who think of ozone as a healthful substance to know that it is one of the prominent components of photochemical air pollution. It is a highly toxic gas even in low concentrations, producing its own typical damage to plants.

Effects on Plant Life

Air pollutants inflict appreciable damage on plant life. In 1956, a group of plant pathologists at the University of California announced that visible injury to plants by atmospheric pollution was causing an annual loss of millions of dollars in California—$3,000,000 in Los Angeles County alone. The statewide loss had increased to $8,000,000 by 1962. The specific contaminants that cause this damage include ethylene, fluorides, oxidized hydrocarbons, ozone, and sulfur dioxide.

Ethylene, for instance, comes from chemical manufacturing processes and motor vehicle exhaust. It causes poor leaf formation, leaf irregularities, and poor flower formation. Its toxicity is also believed to cause the failure of carnation blossoms to open, flower drop in snapdragons, and the withering and drying of petals of some types of orchids.

Sulfur dioxide, known for 75 years as an individual air pollutant, causes severe leaf markings in alfalfa, ruining whole crops of this plant. Leaf markings begin at as low a concentration as 1.25 parts per million for one hour. Cotton and barley are equally sensitive; beans, wheat, carrots, and cabbage need longer exposure to show damage. It is reassuring to know that in Southern California it has been possible to reduce the levels of sulfur dioxide to such a low point that plant damage of this kind does not occur except when there is accidental spilling of sulfur dioxide into the air by an industry.

Trees also are affected. For instance, prune, apricot, and peach trees can be damaged by hydrogen fluoride in concentrations as low as 0.02 to 0.05 parts per million over a long period of time. This is of great concern to growers near industrial operations.

The above are examples of single pollutants. Of even greater concern is the so-called "oxidant damage" typical of California's photochemical smog. This is damage from oxidized hydrocarbons and is of added interest because it is now occurring in other parts of the United States; for example, damage to the tobacco crop in Connecticut and the truck farm crop in New Jersey.

Oxidant damage is recognized by a silvering and glazing of the lower surfaces of leaves, sometimes followed by a reddish discoloration. Brown blotches appear in forage crops such as alfalfa. Many crops—including lettuce, beans, celery, sugar beets, and alfalfa—are affected by it.

Plants may be more sensitive indicators that air pollution is present than either man or animals. Selected species exposed to air pollution can provide information about the chemical nature and concentration of the air pollutants, and damage to certain plants can predict a coming air pollution problem.

Damage to Property

As air pollution increases, so does damage to property. Whole communities can deteriorate because of it. Pittsburgh's and St. Louis' smoke pollution had made both of these cities quite ugly until the aroused citizens determined to do something about it. Air pollution damages property chiefly through the corrosion of metals and deterioration of rubber and other materials. It is possible for sulfur dioxide in air to rot wool, cotton, and leather materials. Works of art can even be affected by air pollution. Smoke is harmful to paintings. Caustic substances in air will deteriorate marble statuary.

Air Pollution Control

What is being done about air pollution? There is currently a great awakening on the part of technical and scientific people and intelligent citizens to the great threat of increasing air pollution. In large metropolitan areas where the problem is recognized, air pollution control agencies have been made responsible for air conservation. Regulations, enforcement, and public education are their responsibility. Industries are increasingly required to install equipment that will cut down on the smoke, gases, and chemicals created by their operations and thrown into the air by their stacks. This equipment is expensive and so, in some places today, industries coming into a community are wisely encouraged to plan for the proper equipment from the very beginning.

Open burning is being forbidden in more and more communities. New York City has even banned the burning of autumn leaves. Sentimental though we may be about this old autumn rite, it does add to air pollution. In Los Angeles the use of backyard incinerators is forbidden.

A recent development in air pollution control is the recognition of the motor vehicle as a major cause of air pollution. Today, chiefly in California, laws are being enacted and put into effect to cut down on the tremendous amount of pollution from the exhausts of automobiles. Good car upkeep and driving help to cut down exhaust emissions, but more is needed. Devices are being developed for installation in autos, trucks, and buses. Other states and the national government are following California's lead. Auto manufacturers are co-operating.

If anyone doubts the necessity for auto exhaust control, he needs only to look at the smog over the morning and late afternoon traffic jams in any city. When autos were a novelty and few in number, they did not matter. Today, their ever-increasing numbers are a major threat to our air supply. In California a crankcase device is already required on all new cars to cut down on "blowby" gases.

Other devices designed to control exhaust contaminants are now undergoing extensive testing. When two or more are approved by state agencies, every motor vehicle in California eventually will be required to carry them. By controlling this major source of pollution, it is hoped that the quality of air will be greatly improved by 1970.

Air Sampling Network

Important to all air pollution control work are sampling stations which provide data as to what is in the air and in what concentrations. The United States Public Health Service receives reports from a countrywide network of such stations, most of which are maintained by local and state air pollution agencies. California agencies maintain some 35 stations. Often, instruments recording weather data are part of a sampling station.

Sampling stations vary in complexity —from those measuring possibly one or two pollutants by simple methods, to others equipped with automatic samplers which measure four or more pollutants continuously. Dust fall, for instance, is sampled by a simple jar method familiar to many science students. Finer particulate matter is measured by a high volume sampler which is much like a glorified vacuum cleaner with special filter paper. Automatic, continuous recorders are generally used to measure such air pollutants as oxidants, sulfur dioxide, carbon monoxide, and oxides of nitrogen.

Standards for Clean Air

One of the most challenging problems in the process of working for clean air in recent years has been that of setting standards for clean air. This pioneer task was undertaken by the State of California. Roughly, this was an attempt to determine what quantity of each given pollutant in a sample of air should be considered the maximum allowable. This test had not been made before to any large extent. Now, values have been set for atmospheric oxidants, carbon monoxide, sulfur dioxide, fluorides, hydrogen sulfide and ethylene. Standards for other pollutants have been postponed until more dependable scientific facilities are available.

The air quality standards will serve as a guide for local communities wishing to maintain a safe supply of air. They will no doubt be referred to in enacting sound air pollution control laws.

Air pollution is a problem in environmental engineering; it is a medical and public health problem; it is a problem of concern to the conservationist and the scientist. But chiefly it is a problem that addresses itself to that larger public which is affected by it and without whose interest and cooperation it cannot be brought under control. The public needs to understand the nature of air pollution. It must create and give support to agencies whose responsibility is the control of air pollution. And also, the public must be ready to cooperate in carrying out the measures to solve the air pollution problem. Some degree of sacrifice may be part of this cooperation.

From the long-range point of view, every community, whether already troubled with an air pollution problem or in the period of rapid growth that almost automatically signals coming problems, needs to plan ahead. Good rapid transit might cut down on the hordes of motor vehicles inching along at peak hours. A concerted effort to ban all kinds of open burning, including outdated methods of collecting and incinerating community rubbish, would be a constructive step. Working with industry to cut down on industrial emissions is essential. New communities can specifically plan so that increase in population and associated industrial development can proceed without exceeding the waste-receiving capacity of their available air. (*See also Oil Pollution*)

—Y.L.

Recommended Reading

Air Pollution: Volumes I and II—Arthur C. Stern, Ed. Academic Press, New York.

Air Pollution and Public Health—Walsh McDermott, M.D. Reprint from *Scientific American*, October 1961. Available from W. H. Freeman and Co., 660 Market Street, San Francisco 4, California.

Teaching Science Through Conservation—M. E. Munzer and P. F. Brandwein, McGraw-Hill, New York.

What's In The Air? Public Affairs Pamphlet 275, 25 cents per copy. Available from Public Affairs Committee, 22 E. 38th Street, New York 16.

ALBACORE

Other Common Names—Tuna, blue-finned tuna, horse mackerel, great albacore

Scientific Name—*Thunnus alalunga*

Family—Scombridae (mackerels and tunas)

Order—Thunniformes

Size—Length, 10½ feet; weight, to 1000 pounds

Range—From the warmer parts of the Atlantic, Pacific, and Indian oceans and the Mediterranean, north to northern Newfoundland, Iceland, and northern Norway

This fish has a strong body about one-quarter to one-sixth as deep as it is long. The body tapers smoothly into the head and more gradually toward the tail fin. The tail fin is broader than it is long and shaped like a boomerang. There are two large dorsal fins. The front dorsal fin is triangular in shape and has thirteen or fourteen interconnected but easily distinguished spines. The rear dorsal fin rises directly behind the front fin, it is comparatively narrow, and it arches back to a sharp-pointed apex. Nine or ten small dorsal finlets follow the rear dorsal fin. Similar anal finlets line the ventral portion of the fish directly behind the anal fin.

The albacore is beautifully colored. Its back is steely blue and its sides and cheeks are silvery. Spots of iridescent pink, green, and other hues tint the sides. Its fins are yellow, black, silvery, and reddish brown in color.

The albacores are very strong and swift swimmers, and can often be seen leaping from the water as they race along singly or in schools. They are highly prized as food fish and many are taken commercially each year. —M.R.

The black-footed albatross, a bird of the open seas, is a master of dynamic soaring

ALBATROSS
Black-footed Albatross
Other Common Names—Gooney, gooney bird
Scientific Name—*Diomedia nigripes*
Family—Diomedeidae (albatrosses)
Order—Procellariiformes
Size—Length, 28 to 36 inches
Range—North Pacific from Kurile Islands, Japan, and the Formosa Channel to Alaska and Baja California, and from the Aleutian Islands and southern Bering Sea nearly to the equator; breeds in the Hawaiian Islands and the Bonin Islands

Of the 13 species of albatrosses, the black-footed is a common visitor to the Pacific Coast of the United States. Also found, but less commonly, is the Laysan albatross, which differs from the black-footed in having a white body. In fully adult plumage the black-footed albatross is a large dusky bird which, at close range, shows a dull white face and white rump and undertail coverts.

All albatrosses are large, goose-sized, heavy-bodied seabirds with exceptionally long and narrow wings fitted to a specialized existence over wide oceans. Aside from the great wings, their most distinctive feature is the stout bill, hooked at the tip, with distinct horny plates, and with the nostrils opening from short tubes on the upper mandible. The largest, the wandering albatross, has a wingspread of nearly 12 feet, not 17 as has often been claimed. Even so, this wingspread makes it the largest flying bird, if size may be measured simply in terms of wingspread.

Albatrosses, often called gooneys or gooney birds, are native to southern oceans, chiefly the South Pacific.

A century ago the short-tailed albatross was the commoner of the two gooneys to reach the offshore waters of the Pacific Coast, but today none of the present generation of birdwatchers in California has ever seen one. For some time it was believed that this white albatross with black wings had become extinct. Before 1900 the Japanese "had done a hellish thing." On one of the Bonins, the "Seven Islands of

Izeu," they killed albatrosses for their feathers and for fertilizer as a business venture. A railway was built to the top of the island and a cableway run to the bay. Every man on the island killed 100 to 200 birds a day until, over a period of years, at least 5,000,000 albatrosses had been slaughtered. Then, in 1903, while the remainder of the birds were away at sea, Olympian reprisal took place. The volcano that dominated the island blew up and every one of the 300 human inhabitants lost his life.

In 1907 the Japanese Government put the short-tailed albatross on the protected list, but the Bonins were so remote that the edict could not be enforced. New settlers came in and resumed killing. By 1932 there were only a few hundred birds left, and in December of that year the inhabitants held one last massacre. The settlers never admitted their guilt, but said that a storm killed the birds. Actually the people had heard that the island was to be declared a bird sanctuary. The next year the island became a Japanese National Monument, but it was too late. In a finishing action, the volcano again erupted in 1939 and wiped the slate clean.

The war years prevented anyone from ascertaining whether any albatrosses survived in the Bonins. Rough seas kept American ornithologist Oliver L. Austin, Jr., from making a landing shortly after the war's end. It was suspected that the bird was extinct. It was therefore a great event when, in 1955, several survivors were discovered on the steep slopes of Tori Shima.

In June 1958, about 14 pairs of short-tailed albatrosses were present and several were nesting there. Every effort was made to protect this precious remnant. All-out hunts were made to eliminate the several stray cats that roamed the island as the Japanese made every effort to retrieve the loss. It was a slow process, for reproduction is slow in albatrosses, but their lives are long.

The albatross is a master of dynamic soaring. If the wind is favorable it is able to skim over the water for a long time without once flapping its wings. Its long slender wings are especially designed for this sort of existence. (*See Bird: Bird Flight.*) In proportion to its size the albatross is not a muscular creature and its cruising range would be limited if it had to rely on its wing beats alone.

When a stiff breeze blows, the albatross can sail against the wind or with it, and is able to quarter a breeze or go directly across it for short distances when under great momentum. When coming against the breeze the wing is bent downward, as if to catch the wind, but when the bird turns and goes with the breeze the wings are fully extended. When sailing against the wind the albatross often rises gradually, and when going swiftly with the wind it usually makes a long swoop downward and skims over the water, thus accumulating speed as it turns to windward.

The food of the albatross includes cuttlefish and other marine animals, and whatever edible refuse it can pick up from the surface of the sea. It follows ships persistently for the purpose of picking up scraps of food thrown overboard, or fishes killed by the ship's propellers, and may often quarrel with its neighbor over these.

The albatross is otherwise usually sociable with its neighbors on its breeding grounds, where it is often intimately associated with other albatrosses, boobies, shearwaters, and terns.

Its nest may be simply a depression in the ground, but more frequently its eggs are laid in a mound of organic matter, composed of earth, grass, moss, feathers, and excrement.

How the Albatross Got Its Name

During the centuries in which England rose to world prominence on the seas, Britain's sailors met with many odd birds. Among the strangest were

The black-footed albatross soars above the Pacific Ocean during most of the year, returning to the sandy beaches of the South Pacific islands only during the brief months of courtship and nesting

members of families seen only in waters of the New World. Some species were prominent in the Pacific, others abounded in the cold regions of the Antarctic. The Portuguese, also great mariners in those days, called all large seabirds *alcatras,* whether these were pelicans, frigate birds, or gooneys. Perhaps some geographer who knew Latin objected to that usage, and basing his argument upon the fact that *albus* was the classical word for white, insisted that the strange white seafowl be called *albatross.*

Just when and how the change was accomplished is not known. It may have been no more than a corruption of *alcatras.* But the new name, now included in numerous languages, first appeared in English about 1769. Within less than a generation the poet, Samuel Taylor Coleridge, had heard legends about the bird's magical powers. In his "Rhyme of the Ancient Mariner," he made the killing of an albatross a major incident. In this way, the seabird, that reportedly becomes seasick when it sits on the deck of a ship, became known to multitudes who had never seen one. —W.B.G.

ALBINISM

To say that not all blackbirds are black, or even that there are occasionally white blackbirds, may seem a contradiction in terms. But this is true because of instances of abnormal coloring in various animals. Albinism, and its opposite, *melanism,* are such instances.

Albinos are individuals that show a lack of normal coloring (pigmentation) and thus appear white or whitish. Technically, this abnormality results from a failure of the body to produce or distribute coloring pigments to the skin, hair, or feathers. This failure is usually genetic (inherited) or it may occasionally result from accident to the tissues involved, improper diet, or even psychological shock. For example, a feather plucked from the tail of a bird when it is not molting (which is the orderly replacement of feathers) may be replaced by a white feather. At the next molt, however, this same feather follicle will

A totally albino red-tailed hawk has no trace of the coloration of its species

produce a normally colored feather.

There are degrees of albinism: (1) Total albinos are entirely lacking in the usual pigmentation, and are thus pure white with pink eyes; (2) partial albinos show complete or partial lack of coloring in certain body areas only, for example, in the tail or the wings. There are also intermediate forms of albinism, including a dilution effect, in which a normally dark bird will be cream-colored rather than white.

A partially albino long-tailed salamander (above) has traces of the dark spots that are normally present (below)

A totally albino white-tailed deer

An albino American toad

The American blackbird family (Icteridae) is particularly susceptible to various degrees of albinism and other color abnormalities. As many as 35 or 40 percent of a flock of red-winged blackbirds may show color abnormalities in their plumage. The proportion of pure albinos—the ones most likely to be noticed—is much lower, but no one has yet calculated how often pure albinos might appear among 100,000 birds. The sparrows, robins, bluebirds, crows, hawks, and to a lesser extent the sandpipers and warblers, are also prone to albinism.

An albino ruby-throated hummingbird

The opposite of albinism is melanism, where all parts are abnormally dominated by dark pigments, so that the animal is dark brown or black. Melanism is less common than albinism. There are, however, a few cases known of birds being partially albinistic and partially melanistic. Excessive yellow pigmentation is called *xanthism;* and excessive red pigmentation produces *erythrism.*

In birds such as canaries and flamingos, which are normally yellowish or pink, dietary deficiencies may cause a "washing out" of plumage to almost white. The addition of paprika or cayenne pepper in olive oil will bring canaries into bright yellow-orange plumage. It has been discovered, also, that captive flamingos that lose color can be brought back to the pink condition by feeding them shrimp. (*See also under Animal: Colors of Animals*) —R.C.C.

ALBINO (*See under Animal: Colors of Animals*)

ALGA

Algae—a large group of plants, mostly aquatic in habit, which includes the familiar seaweeds and several species known only to specialists in algology (the study of algae), including such borderline examples as the one-celled *Euglena* and *Chlorella.* (The word *algae* is plural and never written with an *s*; the singular word is *alga.*)

Being relatively simple plants in both appearance and in their method of reproduction, the algae were once "lumped" together in the phylum Thallophyta with the fungi which are also deceptively simple in appearance. They are both plants without the familiar division of parts into stem, leaves, and roots. But continuing study of the members of these two large groups of plants has revealed that they are so diverse in origin that the term *thallophyte* has little meaning.

Now that they are better known, the tendency is to separate these groups into different phyla, so different are they. Not only are the fungi considered quite separate from the algae, but the algae, also, are classified into several different sub-groups.

This new classification of algae now includes the green algae, which are mostly freshwater forms and include those which form scum on the surface of ponds in summer, as well as the famous *Chlorella*, now being investigated as a producer of food in spaceships. Besides the green algae, other major groups belonging to the algae include the delicate, glass-shelled diatoms that occur in limitless numbers in almost all waters; the euglenoids, which include *Euglena*, the famous specimen organism used in high school and college biology classes to illustrate an organism that can behave, in turn, as either a plant or an animal; another mixed group of single-celled, free-float-

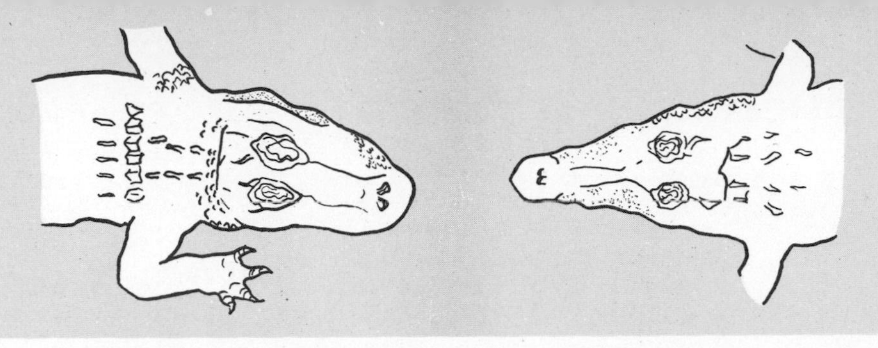

One of the most obvious differences between an alligator and a crocodile is the shape of the snout. That of the crocodile (right) is narrow, in marked contrast to the blunt, rounded snout of the alligator (left).

ing species called dinoflagellates; the familiar red algae of marine environments; the brown algae, which include the largest of all algae, the great marine kelps; and the so-called blue-green algae, which include forms that are sometimes terrestrial rather than aquatic.
—R.C.C.

ALLIGATOR AND CROCODILE
Alligator
American Alligator
Other Common Names—None
Scientific Name—*Alligator mississippiensis*
Family—Crocodylidae (crocodilians)
Order—Crocodilia
Size—Body length, 6 to 12 feet
Range—Coastal regions of the southeastern United States

The American alligator, *Alligator mississippiensis,* was once the longest backboned animal inhabiting the United States. Now it is becoming the scarcest. Areas that formerly supported alligators 19 feet in length are now uninhabited by them. Extremely few survive long enough to perpetuate the species outside Everglades National Park, state parks, and a few private preserves. Captive alligators rarely mate, and they almost never produce offspring. In its native habitat six or seven years elapse after its emergence from egg and nest before an alligator can breed, even though it may increase in length approximately a foot per year during its first decade. Few reptiles as large as a six-foot alligator can stalk their prey at night in the swamps, ponds, lakes, and streams, or bask during the day without becoming the target of a hide hunter.

Were it not for the few havens that afford protection for the American alligator, it would soon be nearing extinction, like its smaller Chinese relative, *Alligator sinensis.* None of the 20 other

Because of overhunting for its hide, the alligator seldom reaches breeding age

Once the longest back-boned animal in North America, the alligator is now scarce

crocodilians has escaped the depredations of man. Human beings have decimated the gavials of Asia, and the caimans of Central and South America, along with the more widely distributed crocodiles.

Crocodile
American Crocodile
Other Common Names—None
Scientific Name—*Crocodylus acutus*
Family—Crocodylidae (crocodilians)
Order—Crocodilia
Size—Body Length, 7½ to 12 feet
Range—Coastal regions of the southeastern United States

In the United States the American crocodile, *Crocodylus acutus,* is restricted largely to a few mangrove swamps at the southern tip of Florida. It fares little better in the lowlands bordering the Pacific Coast, where it was once abundant from Sinaloa southward to Ecuador. Few thriving populations remain in the Atlantic stronghold of the species, between Yucatan and the Magdalena Basin in Colombia. It is doubtful whether Floridian crocodiles ever approached the maximum size of 23 feet they once attained in other parts of their range. Half a century ago, however, they were nearly as abundant as alligators in southern Florida, and far more tolerant

The crocodile is restricted largely to the mangrove swamps of southern Florida

of salt water. Crocodiles could forage in the open sea, and they had the salt-water marshes largely to themselves. They deposited their three-inch eggs in pits they dug in the sand.

Alligators produce smaller eggs, rarely more than 60 in a clutch, and that of a small female may consist of fewer than 30. The female gathers mud and vegetable debris that she heaps into a mound that may be a yard high and six feet across. After the female has used her hind limbs to excavate the summit of the mound, she deposits her eggs in the depression and covers them with more debris. Thereafter, she ordinarily remains in the vicinity of the nest, and apparently attempts to drive off any animals that molest it.

The Chinese and American alligators, though related to the caimans of the American tropics, differ from them in having the nostrils widely separated by bone. Caimans more nearly resemble the crocodiles in this respect, but the arrangement of the teeth readily distinguishes crocodiles from both caimans and alligators. The fifth tooth in the lower jaw of the crocodile is exposed to view because it fits into a notch on the side of the snout when the crocodile closes its mouth. The fifth tooth is hidden rather than exposed in the alligator, for it fits into a pit or socket in the upper jaw.

The crocodile does *not* have its upper jaw hinged. The notion evidently stems from the crocodile's habit of basking with its jaws widely parted. The head must be raised, of course, when the lower jaw is resting on the ground. Alligators bask, either in shallow water or on the bank, but without opening their jaws. Male alligators bellow during the mating season like most, if not all, other crocodilians. The sound does not attract females, but it intimidates other males. Bellowing is an element of crocodilian territorial behavior, therefore, a "proclamation of ownership." Females enter the male's territory with impunity, but intruding males are driven off. —Ch. B.

The stalk of amanita mushrooms rises from a cup that surrounds their base

AMANITA
Orange Amanita
Other Common Names—Royal agaric, Ceaser's agaric
Scientific Name—*Amanita caesarea*
Family—Agaricaceae (fungi with gills)
Range—Southeastern United States
Habitat—Woodlands and pastures with rich soil; from July through September

The orange amanita is one of the few amanitas that is not fatally poisonous. It is related to the death cup, *amanita phalloides,* and to the destroying angel, *amanita verna,* so called because of its whiteness. Amanitas come in many different shades – from white, ranging through greenish, brownish, umber tones, to bright orange, like this one. Since poisonous properties are present at all stages of growth, from button size upward, it is not advisable to eat any mushroom until it is fully grown and can be identified.

This species and all other amanitas grow from a cup that surrounds the stem. No other family of mushrooms has this characteristic, nor do the others have the white spores and gills of this dangerous family. (*See Fungus*).

AMBERJACK

Banded Amberjack
Other Common Names—Rudderfish
Scientific Name—*Seriola zonata*
Family—Carangidae (jacks, scads, and pompanos)
Order—Perciformes
Size—Length, 2 to 3 feet
Range—Along the coast of North America from Cape Cod southward to Cape Hatteras. Also reported in the Gulf of Mexico

The banded amberjack's body is about 3½ times as long as it is deep and it is severely flattened sideways, making the fish very thin. The body tapers forward gradually to the head. The mouth cuts back to the forward edge of the eye and contains rows of hairlike teeth. There are two dorsal fins. The front dorsal fin is small but well developed and it has seven spines. The rear dorsal has 36 to 38 rays and runs from behind the front dorsal fin almost to the tail fin.

The back of the fish is dull blue or silvery brown in color, The sides are paler, and the belly is white. The front dorsal fin is black. The anal fin is white at its base and the tail fin is light green with white tips. While young, the fish has five or six broad vertical blue or brown stripes.

The amberjack follows large fish (particularly sharks), boats, and other floating objects. This is probably because they feed on the leftovers of ocean predators. The fish is often confused with the pilotfish, *Naucrates ductor*, that not only resembles it but has similar habits. The pilotfish, however, has only three or four small spines in its dorsal fin, its gill cover is more rounded than that of the amberjack, and it retains its vertical stripes throughout its entire life.

The great amberjack, *Seriola dumerili*, is a less well-known species. It is found primarily from Florida to Brazil and attains a length of 5 to 6 feet. —M.R.

AMOEBA

Many species of closely related one-celled animals are called amoebas. Most of them are far too small to be seen by the unaided eye, but make excellent subjects for study under the microscope. In general, they are formless bits of protoplasm. The cell membrane stretches to form projections, and the internal fluids flow after them. Any organic debris encountered is ingested through the cell membrane.

Amoebas live in fresh water, the oceans, on most damp surfaces, and even inside other living things. They require a moist environment, but, in periods of dryness, they can enclose themselves in an envelope, called a **cyst,** that prevents the drying out of the living matter. —G.B.S.

AMPHIBIAN

[*Editor's Note:* Biologists define the amphibians as a class of vertebrates whose exisiting members are represented by three orders. The Anura includes all the frogs and toads; the Urodela comprises the newts and the salamanders; and the Apoda has a few species of tropical burrowing animals that lack legs and look like worms.]

On nights following prolonged or heavy rains in the Everglades of Florida, thousands if not millions of frogs assemble at their watery breeding sites. Mating calls reverberate in the hammocks and echo across the ponds in the cypress swamps. An experienced naturalist can often detect the voices of more than a dozen species calling in the neighborhood of one pool. Under favorable conditions the din they produce may be audible at distances of two or three miles. The trills, chirps, bleats, and similar sounds that accompany the reproductive activities of most frogs are almost literally voices from the past. Possibly the dinosaurs foraging in the

Pine-barrens tree frog

swamps of the Cretaceous presented choruses similar to those we hear today.

The first animal that emitted sounds by forcibly expelling the air from its lungs may not have been a frog. It is probable, nevertheless, that such tailless amphibians were issuing their mating calls for at least a hundred million years before our ancestors discovered ways to convey information with the human voice. If the primitives of the Lower Paleolithic had a language, perhaps they also had a name for the creatures we call toads, spadefoots, tree frogs, or simply frogs, when we refer to tailless amphibians as a group.

Amphibians of the Past

Several families of frogs can be traced back millions of years in the fossil record. Thus far, however, no fossils satisfactorily identified as the "first frogs" have come to light. Nearly 200 million years ago one amphibian had a skull closely resembling that of a frog, but this creature scarcely qualifies as an ideal ancestor. Its fossilized skeleton, recovered in Madagascar, shows that it possessed a tail. In other respects it more closely resembled some of the earlier, more primitive amphibians. It may prove to be a representative of a somewhat backward branch of the same stock from which frogs were derived. If other branches were advancing more rapidly, perhaps frogs had already appeared in other parts of the world.

In terms of amphibian history, the frogs, salamanders, and the elongate, limbless caecilians of the tropics, were late comers. The fossil record discloses innumerable earlier amphibians, representatives of groups that appeared and disappeared. Amphibians were once greatly diversified, and some attained impressive dimensions, not recently but back in the days when there were vast swamps where we now have mountains in Pennsylvania. Some 50 million years later, during the Triassic, when the luxuriant vegetation of these swamps was

Swamp tree frog

Cricket frog

Wood frog

turning into coal, the amphibians were still thriving. The skull of one of them from the Triassic exceeded a yard in length. It was called *Mastodonosaurus*, and there is every reason to believe that it was as formidable as its name.

Such goliaths represented an assemblage of weak-limbed, stout-bodied, bottom dwellers with short tails and large heads. Along with many other large amphibians, they were headed for oblivion at the end of the Triassic. Nevertheless the amphibians had been advancing for nearly 200 million years before they declined. When the reptiles arose they began life on land where they deposited their eggs. Amphibians remained tied to the water that cradled their fish-like offspring, although some of them eventually won the fight to remain on land.

Several amphibians became almost wholly aquatic, however, as the reptiles occupied various niches on land. It is questionable, nevertheless, whether either group suffered from competition with the other. Amphibians were holding their own as the reptiles rapidly increased in kind. Later, when reptiles temporarily declined, the amphibians were still thriving. By the time the dinosaurs began to appear, however, and before the winged reptiles called pterosaurs were off the ground, the amphibians declined. A few groups, among them *Mastodonosaurus* and its relatives, faded from the earth. The amphibians, though precariously close to extinction, held on tenaciously.

The spring peeper's voice is produced by inflating the vocal sac on its throat

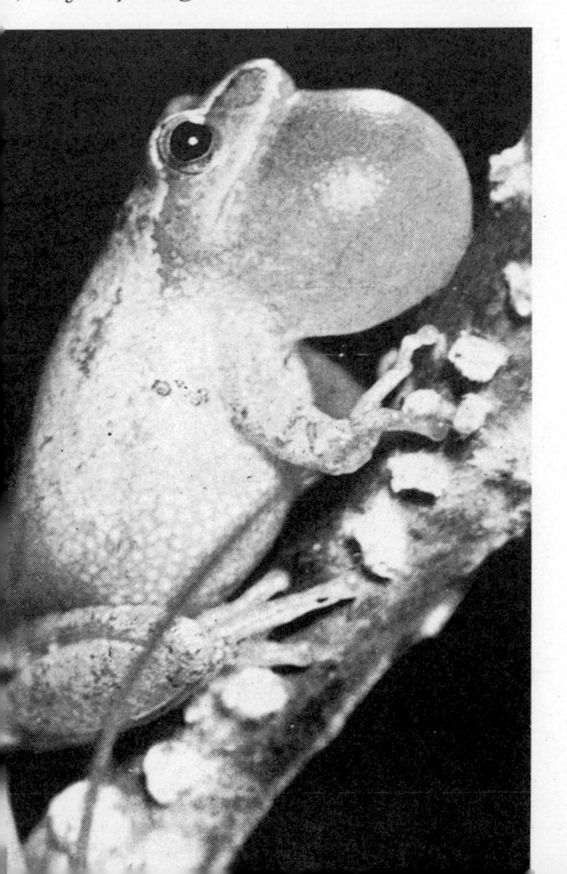

Origin and History

Despite their successful invasion of the land, amphibians never fully recovered from their decline. Only the frogs were destined to become diversified, widely distributed – and sometimes noisy – prior to the advent of man. To understand the problems that confronted the amphibians we must go back to the Devonian, at least 350 million years ago when there were no voices in the swamps. It is highly improbable that the lobe-finned fishes called rhipidistians were vocal. But there are reasons for believing that they had lungs as well as gills before they emerged as the forerunners of the amphibians. If the oxygen became depleted in the pools they inhabited, they could survive by taking in air.

Equally important, these rhipidistians had paired fins that enabled them to push themselves along the pond bottom. Moreover, if the water evaporated in the pool they inhabited, they could move overland to a better pool. If we could have seen one of these cigar-shaped fishes using its lobed fins to propel itself across a mud flat, it is questionable whether we could have foreseen the consequences. This seemingly minor feat marked the turning point in the evolution of the vertebrates. If the only sounds issuing from animals in the Devonian swamps were those of a few insects, the emergence of the amphibians set the stage for the bellowing of crocodiles, and eventually led to the roaring of lions, the songs of birds, and finally, to human speech.

Later on sound played an important role in the behavior of land dwellers. It was an insignificant element of the

The marbled salamander prefers a moist habitat but can survive on dry hillsides

environment during the Devonian, when the transition from fish to amphibian took place. The shift to land opened wholly new vistas. Innumerable habitats remained to be invaded, and the atmosphere afforded a source oxygen that few aquatic vertebrates had managed to tap. Once they had gained a finhold on land, the backboned animals could exploit these advantages. At first locomotion was a laborious process. Even though the lobe-fin of the rhipidistian was a good starting point for the limb of an amphibian, the transition from fin to limb was difficult. It entailed the loss of some bones and the acquisition of others. Those of the toes, for example, appeared as wholly new elements. Before an amphibian could raise its body above the ground and walk, innumerable muscles had to be shifted and coordinated.

Locomotion may have been a relatively minor problem compared to that of finding and seizing prey. Life on land also brought about complex internal changes, in the disposal of waste products and the circulation of the blood, for example. The demands imposed on the terrestrial ancestor of the amphibians led to the three-chambered heart, although one with two chambers had been adequate among the fishes. One need not be astonished that the change-over from the rhipidistian to the amphibian required nearly 20 million years. Amphibians did not simply appear; they gradually emerged during the vast span of the Devonian.

By the end of this geological period it seems probable that the amphibians were advancing along four separate lines. A few million years after the Devonian an offshoot of one line established a trend that led to the reptiles. Other members of this parental group, the labyrinthodonts (the name refers to the complicated enamel patterns in their teeth), continued their advance but retained amphibian traits. They died out before the end of the Paleozoic era, whereas the reptiles went on to flourish in the next era. There were perhaps as many as nine important groups of amphibians toward the end of the Paleozoic, but few of them were left when the Mesozoic era followed. At about the time the lizards appeared, only three rather insignificant groups of amphibians remained. Largely because of their secretive habits, many of those now living remain to be found and described. Thus far approximately 2,500 species are known, but a few more come to light every year.

Amphibians Today

A vast array of backboned animals had already been seen and described when the Swedish naturalist Carolus Linnaeus set out to classify them.

For understandable reasons he relied heavily on superficial resemblances. For instance, he placed caecilians, a few burrowing lizards, and the snakes in the same group because they all lacked limbs. However, he was alluding to the "double lives" of the backboned animals that lived in the water as well as on land, when he coined the name Amphibia in 1735. Originally this encompassed reptiles as well, but it is now reserved for the class of backboned animals that includes only the salamanders, caecilians, and frogs.

Now that more than two centuries have elapsed since Linnaeus provided a name for the class, it does not tax one's ingenuity to distinguish the various orders. Scientists place all those resembling the ancestral amphibians in their possession of limbs and a tail in the order Urodela (or Caudata). These are the salamanders, represented by almost 400 species, of which nearly 90 inhabit the United States. The elongate, or even exceedingly slender creatures, are called caecilians and assigned to the order Apoda (or Gymnophiona). All of the caecilians are limbless, a few are eel-like and aquatic. Most, perhaps a hundred species, are burrowing, secretive animals. Finally the widely distributed tail-less amphibians designated categorically as frogs are grouped in the order Anura (or Salientia). More than 2,000 species may prove to be recognizable, of which almost 70 inhabit the United States.

Amphibians have the dubious distinction of being represented now by fewer species than any other class of backboned animals. Mammals do not quite outnumber the amphibians two to one, however. By virtue of the heat that mammals generate internally, they can tolerate a wide range of environments. In contrast, the amphibians have exploited the advantages of being cold-blooded. Much of the food required to support a mammal or a bird is converted into heat. Amphibians derive sufficient heat to meet their needs from the soil, water, air, or directly from the sun. Consequently they consume far less food than birds and mammals. Where two or three insect-eating mammals might subsist in an acre of land, the same area might support at least 30 or 40 frogs.

In their lack of internal heat the amphibians resemble fishes on the one hand and the reptiles on the other. Though reptiles are armored with plates or horny scales, amphibians are naked. Fur or feathers insulate the birds and mammals that can ill afford to lose much of the heat they generate. However, moisture loss rather than heat loss dictates the behavior of amphibians. The skin of the amphibian is far from being so nearly impervious as that of a reptile. Amphibians lack skins that retard the loss of moisture for reasons easily explained.

The skin afforded one way for the amphibians to assimilate more oxygen. As they dispensed with the scales of their rhipidistian ancestors, their three-chambered hearts pumped blood to the skin as well as to the lungs. The blood of all amphibians now courses through an extensive network of capillaries in the skin. Oxygen dissolved in the mucus that covers the body reaches the corpuscles beneath the surface. Like lung surfaces, the skin must be moist to absorb oxygen. The amphibian's skin is well supplied with mucous glands, however, and these release a moist, sticky substance on the surface.

Because of the mucous covering their bodies, some amphibians are slippery. Anyone who attempts to seize a slimy salamander, *Plethodon glutinosus,* a species widely distributed in the United States from Texas eastward, discovers that it readily slides out of his hands. Aquatic salamanders are equally well equipped to elude capture. Whether amphibians live in the water, inhabit land, or go from one to the other, their skins are perpetually moist. The members of the largest family (Plethodontidae) of salamanders are particularly dependent on oxygen absorbed through their moist skins. They draw in air through their nostrils by means of muscles in their throats. Because all salamanders in this one family lack lungs, however, any oxygen derived from this air passes through the lining of the mouth.

The elongate, snake-shaped caecilians further resemble most snakes in having one lung rather than the usual pair. All caecilians have dispensed with limbs and one lung, but some retain a few rows of fishlike scales. Since these are well hidden below the skin of such caecilians, they are as naked as other amphibians. The relatively greater area of skin on the long, slender body of a caecilian may compensate for the loss of one lung.

So all amphibians are naked animals with moist, glandular skins. Although they lack special mechanisms to provide internal heating, small amounts of heat result from muscular action and digestion. When an amphibian is submerged in mud or when it is in air saturated with moisture, its body may be slightly warmer than its environment. If an amphibian is exposed to dry air, however, its body temperature drops. It closely approximates the level a thermometer reaches when the bulb is covered with a moist cloth. In other words, both amphibians and wet-bulb thermometers are cooled by evaporation. Heat is transferred from the amphibian's body to the water as it is vaporized and carried off in the ambient air.

Where Amphibians Live

Rates of evaporation diminish as the amount of moisture in the air increases. Understandably, therefore, land-dwelling amphibians are most abundant in humid environments. When relative humidities reach maximum levels in such habitats as rain forests, very little water is lost from the skin. Because the amphibian's body is very slightly warmer than the air when it is saturated, evaporation continues, but at a very low rate. Moreover, small amounts of water are expelled with waste products. It follows that no amphibian can be exposed to air for prolonged periods without replenishing the water in its body.

Several North American salamanders, among them the hellbender (*Cryptobranchus*), the waterdogs and mudpuppies (*Necturus*), and the Texas blind salamander (*Typhlomolge*) and a few other members of its family (Plethodontidae) remain in the water. Some caecilians and frogs have also forsaken land habitats. Other amphibians alternate between land and water, or at least they return to a stream or pool only when they breed. Most caecilians and many salamanders and frogs spend their entire lives on land. Unlike their early ancestors, they are no longer chained to the water by their offspring. As we shall see farther on, some amphibians begin life on land, where they forage and reproduce.

The need for maintaining a moist skin

while avoiding excessive water loss imposes restrictions on amphibians. They do not drink, but they must have access to moisture, be it mud, wet sand, or droplets of dew on a rock or leaf surface Amphibians deficient in water absorb it either by flattening the body on a moist surface, by backing into the wet sand or mud, or by sitting in a puddle or a pool. They cannot absorb it from the air, even when it is saturated. A complex mechanism controlled by the pituitary gland prevents amphibians from absorbing too much water.

If its skin were removed, an amphibian would not lose moisture any more rapidly. Consequently amphibians are most active when ground is moist. Or they make forays from the vicinity of water to which they can return and replenish their supply. During the dry season they retreat below the surface, or they seek shelter beneath leaves, bark, or in cavities that remain moist. Some swamps, of course, are wet continuously. Other amphibian strongholds, also environments that are almost perpetually wet, are the rain forests and cloud forests of the tropics. A few salamanders inhabit caves or underground pools. Such habitats are not wholly ideal, however, because of the meager food supply.

The boreal toad, *Bufo b. boreas*, reaches Alaska, and occurs at elevations of 10,000 feet in Colorado. The distributions of one salamander, the northern rough-skinned newt, *Taricha g. granulosa*, and one frog, the wood frog, *Rana sylvatica*, also extend to Alaska. In Europe frogs occur within the Arctic Circle, but only in areas where the subsoil is not permanently frozen. The true frogs, *Rana*, and tree frogs, *Hyla*, are well represented in the humid eastern portion of the United States. In the deserts of the southwestern states they exist around a few streams or springs. The toads (*Bufo*) and the spadefoots, (*Scaphiopus*) have penetrated many of the most arid regions. They manage to survive, in fact to thrive, in areas where rain is sporadic and uncertain. A year or more may elapse between periods when enough rain falls to produce the temporary pools in which they spawn.

In areas subject to drought, or when the temperature of the environment drops to levels near freezing, many amphibians descend well below the sur-

The aquatic red-spotted newt lives ashore as a larval red eft, one to three years

face. In the semi-tropical climate of southern Florida tree frogs often seek shelter during the winter beneath bark or leaves. During severe winters, however, green tree frogs, *Hyla cinerea,* hidden too near the surface are killed when air temperatures drop to abnormal levels. Tree frogs of the same species near the northern extremity of the range in Maryland differ in their habits. If the majority of the individuals in the northern populations sought to spend the winter so near the surface, these populations would be decimated within a year or so.

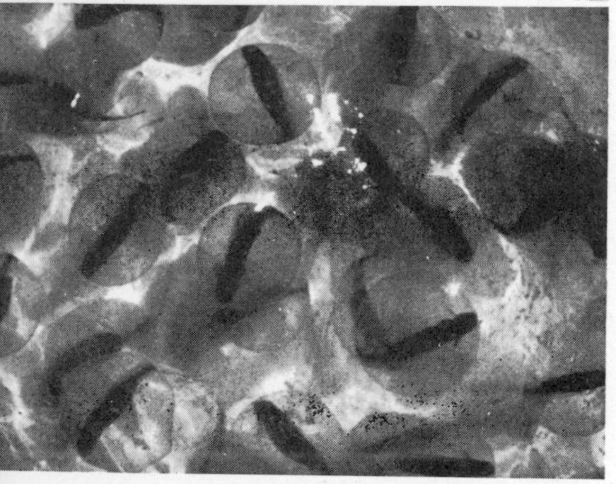

Embryos of spotted salamanders

A dusky salamander guards her eggs

Modes of Reproduction

At least some members of every major group of backboned animals lay eggs. Whether they deposit their eggs in water, on land, or in situations above or below the surface of the ground, the eggs are likely to be destroyed or eaten. Egg-layers greatly outnumber but seldom outsmart the egg-eaters, who have evolved ways of finding eggs almost as rapidly as the vertebrates have evolved ways of concealing or guarding them. Eggs can be, and in some animals are, effectively protected if they are retained inside the body of the female during the development of the embryo. This, of course, is the mode of reproduction characteristic of all mammals except the platypus and the spiny anteaters that lay eggs and, hence, are oviparous.

Mammals have no monopoly on viviparity, there are live-bearers among fishes, amphibians, reptiles. Presumably the primitive amphibians all laid their eggs in the water. Their gilled offspring, like the tadpoles one knows today, were also fish-like in habits until their limbs and lungs developed. They were ill-equipped to leave the natal pool until they were beyond the fish stage and prepared to breathe and move about on land. The life histories of many amphibians are still much like those of their ancestors. But numerous frogs and salamanders and nearly all the caecilians have abandoned such habits, or modified them in some fashion.

Eggs laid in pools are exposed to parasites as well as predators. Several other animals ranging from insects to fishes, birds, frogs, and salamanders destroy or devour amphibian eggs, or prey on their aquatic larvae. In Panama and Brazil male tree frogs of one species excavate basins or "nests" at the edges of shallow streams where the females deposit their eggs. Other members (*Agalychnis*) of the tree frog family in Mexico and Central America deposit their gelatinous clumps of eggs on the under-

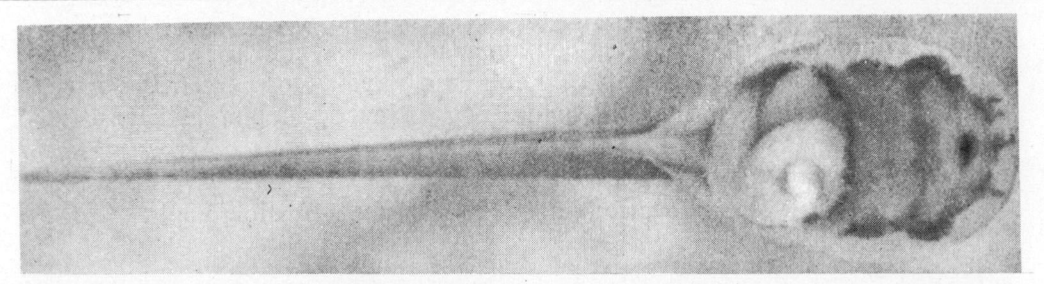

The internal organs of the spring peeper tadpole can be seen through its skin

surface of leaves overhanging streams. Their tadpoles develop before heavy rains wash them into the water from the egg capsules. Naturalists searching at night for frogs have come upon cat-eyed snakes (*Leptodeira*) devouring these clumps of eggs.

Perhaps frogs evolved ways to carry their eggs or offspring in response to the difficulties of avoiding such predators. After fertilizing the eggs expelled by the female, the male European midwife toad, *Alytes obstetricans*, thrusts one leg and then the other through the mass. Thereupon he returns to his moist burrow with the eggs adhering to his legs. On occasions when the surface is wet the eggs absorb moisture when the male emerges. The tadpoles are well advanced about 20 days later when the male carries the tadpoles to water. Thereupon they burst out of the capsules and shift for themselves.

At seasonal intervals several frogs in the American tropics are converted into animated nurseries. The female of Darwin's frog, *Rhinoderma darwini*, lays from five to fifteen eggs, all of them large. After fertilizing them the male takes them into his mouth, where they pass through a slit beneath the tongue and enter the vocal sac. The male carries them in this distensible sac until the young are fully formed, then expels them by returning them to the mouth through the slit. In contrast, the female, rather than the male, of the marsupial tree frogs (*Gastrotheca*) carries the developing eggs. She uses her hind legs to shove the fertilized eggs into a purse-like pocket on her back. The young are ready to leap forth in search of their food when they emerge.

Surinam toads, *Pipa pipa*, though almost wholly aquatic, transport their eggs and developing young in pockets in the female's back. While the male clasps the female, both of them repeatedly swim upward in an arc that results in their turning upside down as they approach the water's surface. At such times the female expels eggs that descend slowly enough to permit the pair to swim beneath the eggs. Many of the whitish, sticky spheres land on her back, where each induces a pocket to form in the skin. As the eggs sink into the skin, a protective covering or lid derived from the egg capsules forms on each pocket. The developing offspring pass through all their larval stages in their individual pockets. Several weeks later they emerge as tiny replicas of their parents.

Males of the distantly related forest frogs (*Dendrobates* and *Phyllobates*) in the American tropics carry tadpoles on their backs. After the eggs have hatched in small pockets of water off the ground, the tadpoles are well developed before the male carries them to pools or streams. The robber frogs (*Eleutherodactylus*) and the cliff frogs (*Syrrhophus*), each with two species that reach the United States, circumvent the need to transport their tadpoles to water. They lay relatively huge eggs in moist places on land, in caves, or in crevices on cliffs. A species introduced in Florida from the West Indies, *Eleutherodactylus ricordi*, so often lays its eggs in flower pots that it has become known as the greenhouse frog. Each of the large eggs contains enough yolk to support the developing occupant until it emerges as a froglet.

Woodland salamanders (*Plethodon*) and many of their relatives emerge fully formed from large eggs. The female often coils around her eggs, perhaps to guard them or to keep them moist. The oak salamander, *Aneides lugubris*, of the Pacific Coast may lay its eggs on the ground or deposit them in cavities in trees. Each of a dozen or more eggs is attached to the roof of the cavity by a gelatinous thread. Some of the limbless caecilians also coil their slender bodies around their clutches of eggs, but others bring forth living young. The only live-bearing amphibians in the Americas are caecilians. Others inhabit Africa, the only continent that supports live-bearing frogs, members of the genus *Nectophrynoides*. Salamanders are far more diversified in North America than in Europe. Nevertheless the only salamanders that retain their eggs in the body until their larvae are fully formed are European. The black salamander, *Salamandra atra*, regularly retains the eggs in the body until the young are fully formed. A close relative, the fire salamander, *Salamandra maculosa*, retains its eggs only when it cannot reach the streams where it ordinarily deposits its eggs.

Despite all these departures from ancestral habits, many of the amphibians in the United States hew closer to the line. The two-lined salamander, *Eurycea bislineata*, attaches its eggs singly to the underside of rocks in cold mountain brooks. The Pacific newt, *Taricha torosa*, lays small clumps of eggs attached to twigs in the water. Some mole salamanders (*Ambystoma*) also follow much the same procedure. In eastern North America, however, the red-spotted newt, *Notophthalmus viridescens*, deposits its eggs one at a time, fasten-

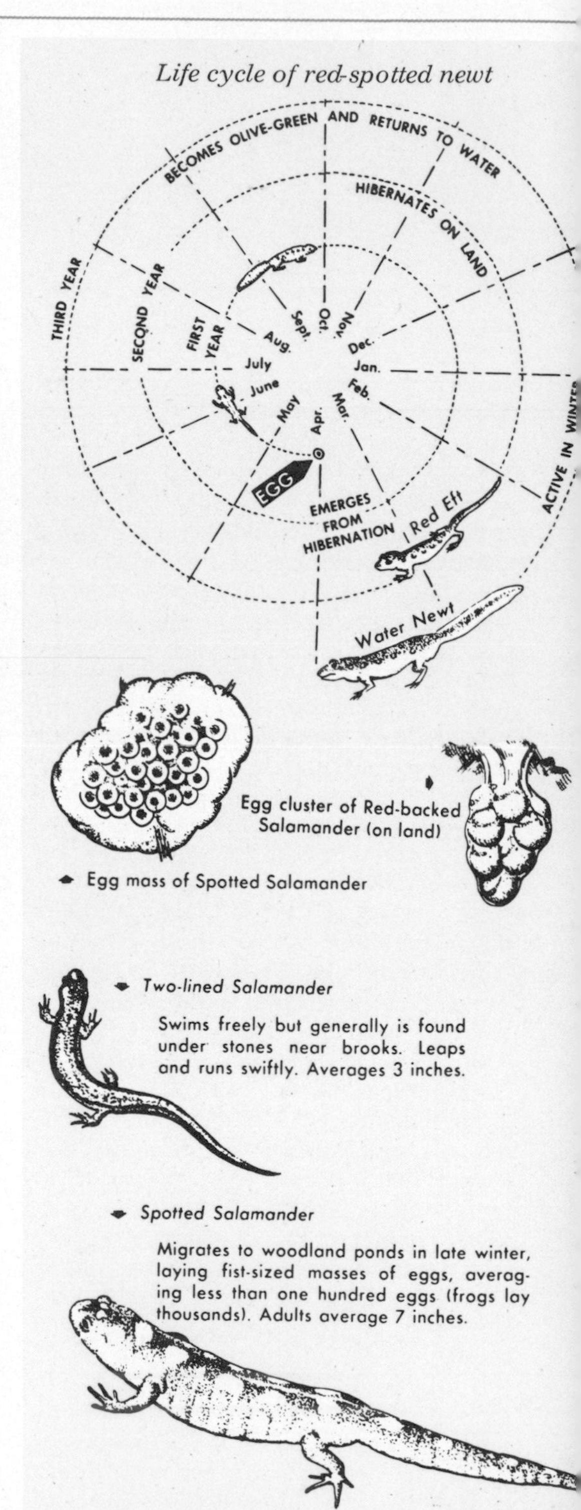

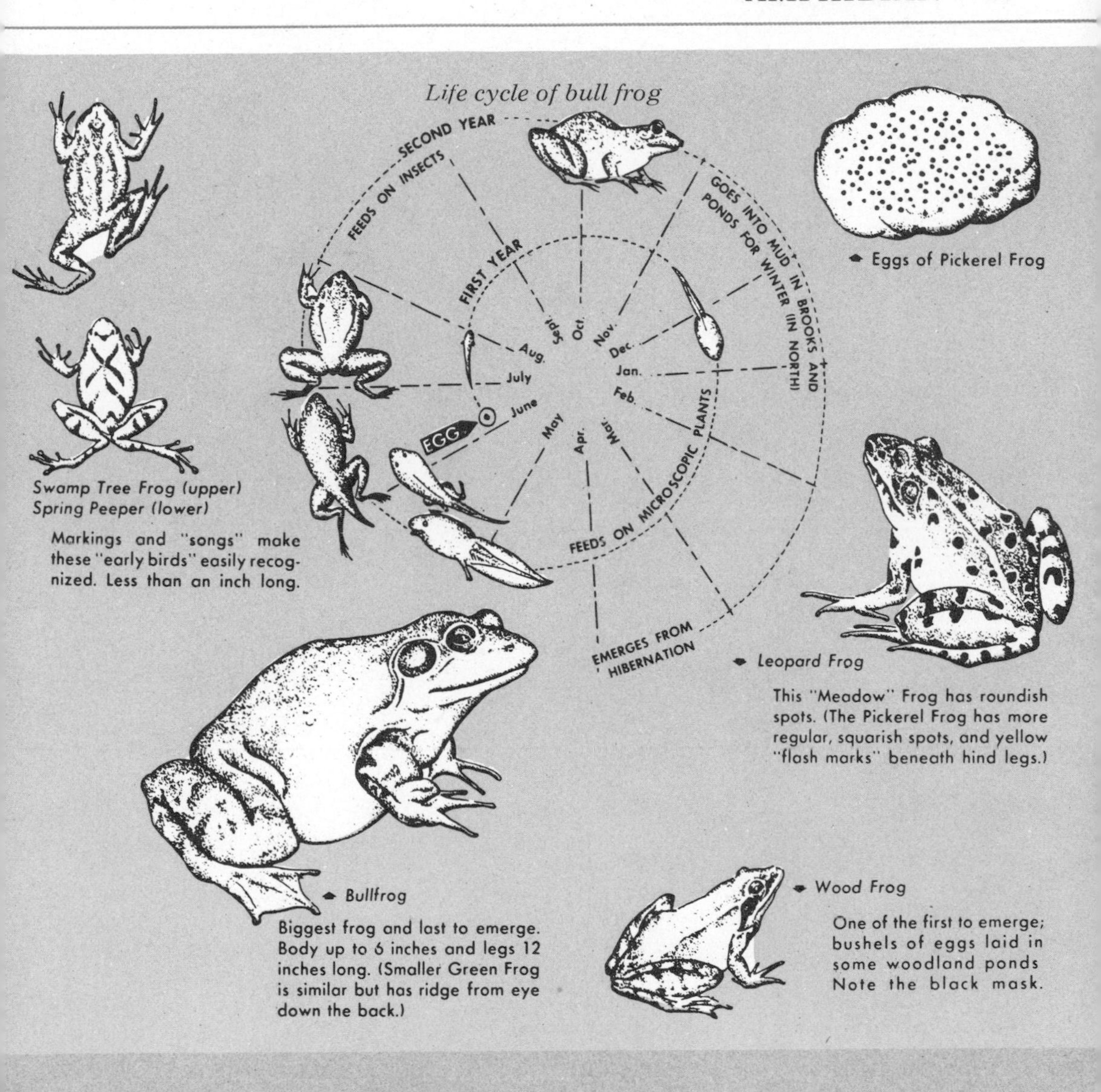

Swamp Tree Frog (upper)
Spring Peeper (lower)

Markings and "songs" make these "early birds" easily recognized. Less than an inch long.

Eggs of Pickerel Frog

Leopard Frog

This "Meadow" Frog has roundish spots. (The Pickerel Frog has more regular, squarish spots, and yellow "flash marks" beneath hind legs.)

Bullfrog

Biggest frog and last to emerge. Body up to 6 inches and legs 12 inches long. (Smaller Green Frog is similar but has ridge from eye down the back.)

Wood Frog

One of the first to emerge; bushels of eggs laid in some woodland ponds Note the black mask.

Toad eggs

Toad

All true toads have rough warty skins (but they do not cause warts).

Tree "Toad"

The Tree "Toad" is really a frog. Its toes have enlarged tips, making it a good climber.

Male in song

ing each to a leaf or plant in the pool. Most toads lay their eggs in two long strings, one from each oviduct.

The red-spotted toad, *Bufo punctatus*, of the southwestern deserts lays its eggs singly, however, and the oak toad, *Bufo quercicus*, in Florida and the extreme Southeast lays from two to six eggs that form a rod rather than a string. Most spadefoots (*Scaphiopus*) in the United States attach their eggs to debris in temporary pools. The great basin spadefoot, *Scaphiopus intermontanus*, utilizes streams, ponds, and permanent pools. However, the other four species depend largely upon the temporary pools that form after heavy rains.

The eastern spadefoot toad is dependent on temporary ponds formed by rain

True frogs of the genus *Rana* are largely restricted to permanent water. Most of the 16 species deposit eggs in a clump usually anchored to the vegetation. The size of the egg cluster varies extensively. Commonly there is still ice on the ponds when wood frogs, *Rana sylvatica*, breed in March in the northeastern United States. Their small clumps of approximately 1,000 eggs are usually a few inches below the surface. In contrast, the much larger bullfrog, *Rana catesbeiana*, deposits a huge mass of eggs that spreads out on the surface. Exceptionally large masses cover five square feet and contain at least 20,000 eggs. The body of a large female wood frog is scarcely more than three inches long, but along the Gulf Coast it is not unusual for female bullfrogs to attain body lengths of eight inches.

Plainly the amphibians are extremely adaptable creatures. They have overcome many of the restrictions imposed by their absorption of oxygen through a skin that must be kept moist. Notwithstanding this handicap, the shapes, habits, and behavior of the amphibians have become modified in ways that permit them to survive under an impressive array of environments. A talented author who recently described amphibians as "dull creatures indeed, seemingly without enterprise, aspiration or conspicuous resourcefulness" was plainly confused.

Amphibian achievements are, of course, attributable to the effects of natural selection rather than to their "aspirations." Frogs did not set out to become leaping animals. If they "leaped their way to success" they did so because of a complex interplay of the effects of their environments and differences in survival rates and reproductive capacities. In a word, the numerous and varied specializations of the amphibians are attributable to selection. This in turn is most aptly defined as "a device for generating a high degree of improbability." Had it not happened to a few of them, it would seem improbable that amphibians could dispense with limbs or lungs.

Senses and Courtship

The stentorian voice of the male barking tree frog, *Hyla gratiosa*, attracts the female of the species. Not every female responds, however, for mating calls attract only those ready to deposit their eggs. When torrential summer rains flood the depressions in the pine flatwoods of central Florida, hordes of frogs, toads, and tree frogs emerge with the onset of darkness. The clamor produced by a hundred or more large barking tree frogs, however, easily exceeds that of several other species that often call, clasp, expel, and fertilize their eggs in the same pond. When four or five inches of rain have fallen, these breeding aggregations commonly reappear in full force for two or three nights. After that the volume of sound usually diminishes.

At the spawning site, female barking tree frogs behave as though they were oblivious of all sounds except the calls issuing from males of the same species. Each female works her way through the vegetation to reach a vociferous male. He repeats the mating call, which is issued each time air is forced from his lungs over the vocal cords and through the mouth to the vocal sac covered by distensible skin on his throat. This sac acts as a resonator when it is fully inflated, and momentarily it resembles a balloon. It rapidly deflates, however, as the air is returned to the lungs, and promptly reexpands when the next call is issued.

Successive calls from the same source afford the female with a means of orienting her movements. As she approaches the male he sees her, or sometimes becomes aware of her presence when she touches him. It is uncertain whether scent influences the male's reaction. Normally, however, he stops calling, grasps the approaching female, and remains with her until he fertilizes the eggs she extrudes.

While some female barking tree frogs are spawning, however, others are either devouring insects or remain hidden a few yards away. Such females may have spawned on previous days, or they may be too young to deposit their eggs. Regardless of their age, they continue to avoid breeding aggregations until the night arrives when they have mature eggs in their oviducts, and another storm wets the soil and fills the ponds.

This situation illustrates some of the complexities of amphibian behavior. While the external environment is changing from night to day, from season to season, and from one year to the next, internal changes are taking place in each individual. The activities of each amphibian, what any individual does, depends upon the interplay of the conditions that prevail inside and outside its body. A frog is affected by amounts of heat, light, moisture, or food that are, or have been, available. How the frog is affected, however, may depend upon its ancestry.

The several species of frogs in New England, for example, do not start to breed simultaneously. Ordinarily the spring peeper, *Hyla crucifer*, calls first. Other species emerge in regular sequence as the ponds become warmer. The last one to breed is also the largest, the bullfrog, *Rana catesbeiana*. Some species have shorter breeding seasons than others, but each female deposits only one clutch of eggs. In Florida and along the Gulf Coast, however, many kinds of frogs emerge and breed whenever it rains, from April to September. Thus far, no one has discovered whether the same female spawns repeatedly. The females of one species from Algeria can spawn five times in succession, however, at intervals of less than three weeks.

It is evident, therefore, that seasonal changes affect the behavior of amphibians in obvious as well as subtle ways. Female frogs not in suitable condition to respond to mating calls may nevertheless hear them. Perhaps all species are not equally sensitive, but green frogs, *Rana clamitans*, are aware of sounds that range in frequency from 30 to 15,000 cycles per second. Probably frogs are aware of most of the sounds that human beings hear. Nearly all frogs have an exposed eardrum, but this is lacking in salamanders. Consequently they were believed to be deaf, but it has been shown that some, and perhaps all, salamanders can hear. They may be unaware of sounds at frequencies much above 1,000 cycles per second, however. A few salamanders make faint noises, perhaps accidentally. The Pacific giant salamander (*Dicamptodon*), which can emit a feeble barking sound, is the only species definitely known to have vocal cords. Caecilians too are silent, but they may be aware of sounds transmitted through the soil.

Frogs are the only amphibians that engage in noisy breeding activities. Their mating calls are readily interpreted as a highly specialized form of courtship. Sound is less important than other senses in the lives of salamanders and caecilians. Almost nothing has been learned about senses in caecilians, although it is virtually certain that the tentacles on the head have some sensory function. The eyes are greatly reduced or virtually missing in some species. Without vision, caecilians presumably find their prey by means of scent, but sound cannot be ruled out. Vision is important to terrestrial salamanders and frogs, but motionless animals escape the attention of frogs. Perhaps scent is more important to salamanders, particularly those inhabiting the darkness of caves where eyes are useless. The blind species obviously find their prey in caves without benefit of vision. Pacific newts (*Taricha*) apparently depend largely upon scent in finding their way to and from one particular pool. They manage to return to the same pool even when they are captured and released five miles from it.

If these newts can find their way home by a sense of smell, other salamanders that deposit their eggs in water may smell their way to breeding sites. The migrations of mole salamanders (*Ambystoma*) lead to courting activity before they spawn in shallow pools. The males arrive first, and move about actively in the water, rubbing against one another. It is uncertain whether they emit any odor that attracts the females who arrive later. However, the odd behavior of the males seems to excite the females. The activities of the males, therefore, lead to the fertilization and deposition of the eggs.

Courtships also precede the deposition of eggs by terrestrial salamanders that carry out their breeding activities entirely on land. Couples rather than groups participate. The male, perhaps attracted to the female by her scent, approaches her head. He rubs his head and neck against her throat and snout before the onset of the so-called "tail walk." Perhaps the rubbing serves to arouse the female. As the courtship proceeds she follows the male as he moves about with his back arched and his tail extended between her forelimbs. Eventually the male pauses and expels a gelatinous cone capped by a packet of sperm. When the pair moves forward, the female, her throat now pressing against the base of the male's tail, lowers the rear of her body over the packet of sperm, and draws the male germ cells into her vent.

In most terrestrial salamanders the spermatozoa reach small pockets in the lining of the vent. They remain until the eggs pass these pockets and are fertilized in passing; they are then discharged from the oviducts. In the live-bearing salamanders, however, the spermatozoans move into the oviducts to fertilize the eggs. The male of the tailed frog, *Ascaphus truei*, of the American Northwest appears to have a short tail. It is employed to fertilize the eggs of the female before they are deposited. The African frogs that retain their eggs inside the body lack the "tail", yet their eggs are fertilized internally in some fashion that remains mysterious.

In most habitats occupied by amphibians, soil and water temperatures are more important than air temperatures. Aquatic salamanders are occasionally seen swimming beneath the ice in New England. Wood frogs, *Rana sylvatica*, issue their mating calls and deposit their eggs in March while ice remains on the ponds in New Jersey and the water is barely above freezing. When the surface temperatures approach this level many terrestrial salamanders seek

Common tree frog

cover. Tiger salamanders, *Ambystoma tigrinum*, are evidently tolerant of lower temperatures. Hundreds of them were observed participating in a migration in Nebraska while a storm covered the ground with an inch or so of snow. Amphibians nevertheless fail to survive body temperatures two or three degrees below freezing. Frogs from warm climates are unable to move at temperatures a few degrees above freezing. Prolonged exposure to such temperatures kills tropical frogs, though leopard frogs, *Rana pipiens*, survive under the same conditions.

Salamanders exercise little if any control over their body temperatures between the extremes that drive them to cover. Few of them remain abroad when temperatures approach 90° Fahrenheit. Toads and tree frogs tolerate somewhat higher body temperatures, but they appear to be more sensitive to changes. Fowler's toad, *Bufo woodhousei fowleri*, tends to maintain its body temperature at a level of 75° F. while it is foraging, although its activities cover a much wider range. Fowler's toad breeds before the water in the ponds is much above 60°, but later than the American toad, *Bufo americanus*, which tolerates lower temperatures.

In air saturated with moisture the barking tree frog, *Hyla gratiosa*, survives for at least 24 hours with its body temperature near 100°. At such levels its body is pale yellow, though it is more nearly brownish while in cool water, and usually green or gray when it is above ground at temperatures near 80° Tree frogs exhibit a wide range of color changes than most other frogs and toads. Amphibians, with few exceptions, are darker at low temperatures in humid environments than they are when exposed to dry air and high temperatures. Nearly all amphibians seek cover when they are exposed to currents of dry air.

On the whole, therefore, amphibians are endowed with most of the senses encountered in the higher backboned animals. They react to changes in their environments in ways that enhance their chances of surviving. This, as we have seen, is something that amphibians as a group have been doing for an extremely long time.

Growth and Size

The wide range in the size and shape of amphibians reflects their various modes of existence. Each species becomes adjusted to its environment in its own way. Changes in life histories and behavior usually accompany changes in size or shape. Consequently some distinctive combination of traits characterizes each species. Specialized modes of existence often affect the eggs and larvae as well as the adults. The species that protect their developing offspring, whether they are carried in the "built-in nurseries" or remain in the oviducts, tend to produce few eggs. The black salamander, *Salamandra atra*, an inhabitant of the Alps in Europe, gives birth to only two or three young. These are nourished in the female's body at the expense of other eggs that fail to develop.

The eggs of amphibian species which deposit them in moist places on land are relatively large. They are commonly hidden in cavities, crevices, or beneath rocks, where they are normally exposed to fewer hazards than those deposited in water. For this reason, perhaps, there are seldom many eggs in a clutch. Twelve to fifteen eggs deposited in summer by the pigmy salamander, *Desmognathus wrighti*, are enough to perpetuate this inhabitant of spruce-fir forests in the Great Smoky Mountains. As implied by the vernacular name, it is a small salamander, the smallest in the United States, scarcely two inches long, including the tail. It might be expected that the smallest salamander would lay the fewest eggs. Nevertheless, much larger terrestrial salamanders, as well as burrowing caecilians a foot or more in length, produce as few as 20 eggs.

The cliff frog, *Syrrhophus marnocki*, deposits eight to twenty eggs in moist crevices in the limestone of southern Texas. Female cliff frogs seldom exceed an inch and a half in length. This is twice the maximum length of the smallest frog in the United States, the little grass frog, *Limnaoedus ocularis*. The largest females of this tiny species, which breeds in shallow pools in Florida and the coastal lowlands to the north, may deposit more than a hundred eggs. A far more bulky amphibian, the Colorado River toad, *Bufo alvarius*, inhabits the Sonoran Desert of Mexico, Arizona, and California. This toad, the largest in the United States, attains a body length of seven inches, and lays as many as 8,000 eggs. It is exceeded in length, and possibly also in bulk, by the American bullfrog, *Rana catesbeiana*. Along the Gulf Coast, and in some areas where bullfrogs have been introduced west of the Rocky Mountains, females at the maximum size of eight inches produce as many as 20,000 eggs.

It would be miraculous, to say the least, if all these eggs hatched and produced tadpoles that transformed and lived to reproduce. The country would also be a mess, for much of it would be inundated with bullfrogs. Contrary to what misguided individuals assume when they purchase a pair of bullfrogs hopefully expecting to establish a frog farm, not all of the 20,000 eggs hatch. Furthermore, an extremely small percentage of those that emerge from the eggs ever get beyond the tadpole stage. The bullfrog, it would seem, compensates in advance for the loss by producing eggs in large quantities. This is only part of the story, however.

The situation becomes more comprehensible if one compares the life history of the bullfrogs with that of other amphibians. First one must consider the amphibians that lay perhaps 20 or 30

Its body submerged, the bullfrog keeps an eye on things with its periscope-like eyes

eggs in moist secluded places on land. Female salamanders and caecilians often coil around the eggs and thereby protect them from desiccation and perhaps also from parasites or small predators. The eggs contain sufficient yolk to nourish the larvae throughout their development. When the fully formed offspring emerge a couple of months later they can crawl or hop, seek food or cover, or do nearly everything their parents can do except breed. Two years later, however, they may be ready to do even this.

By contrast, the eggs of the bullfrog, with favorable conditions, hatch in three days. Gilled larvae that swim forth from the egg capsules are normally destined to remain as tadpoles for at least two years, or even three. In some areas they do not transform until the tadpole has been imprisoned below ice for three successive winters. By now larvae from any one clutch have been decimated. The few that survive must now forage on land and elude predators for an additional two, three, or four years before they are ready to spawn. Meanwhile, many of the smaller bullfrogs will have been devoured by snakes and other predators, including larger bullfrogs. Perhaps there are at best three or four individuals from any clutch that survive the eight years required to attain maximum size.

Except for the protracted larval stages and the time required to reach maturity, the life history of the bullfrog differs in few respects from that of 15 other closely related species (of the genus *Rana*) that inhabit the United States. All of them deposit their eggs in pools or streams, where each of their progeny is sporadically if not continuously subjected to hazards of one sort or another from the moment the egg is fertilized. Life perhaps is less perilous for the bullfrog as it approaches its maximum size, however. Water snakes, *Natrix sipedon*, for example, that prey on the bullfrog's tadpoles, are unable to subdue a large adult bullfrog. One approaching its maximum size might also be more successful in eluding predators, but not merely because it is stronger and can leap farther than a young bullfrog. The larger frog may also leap sooner, or it may even have found better alternatives.

Learning plays a significant role in survival. Like the burnt child that dreads the fire, a frog that survives an encounter with a snake may not be easily approached by another snake. The behavior of individuals of the same species, particularly those of the same sex at any one locality, tends to be similar. No two individuals are exactly alike in size, shape, or color, nor do they have identical histories. Consequently no two individuals will have modified their behavior in precisely the same way. Aside from the element of learning, the frogs that were least adept at escaping predators at the time of their transformation were also least likely to survive. Natural selection is a continuous process. Hence, the frog that tends to live the longest is nearly always one that was better endowed than others at the outset.

Changes in the habits, behavior, or even the life histories of amphibians often accompany changes in climatic conditions. Some of the frogs that inhabit the deserts presumably evolved slowly along with the arid climates. Couch's spadefoot, *Scaphiopus couchi*, is one of the few amphibians that inhabits the most arid regions along the Mexican border without being restricted to the vicinity of permanent pools or streams. It thrives in areas where rains sufficiently heavy to create pools are sporadic. Furthermore, the largest pools that form may be gone a month later. The tadpoles of a bullfrog would disappear along with the pool, but not the spadefoot's. Its tadpoles can transform, sometimes still with remnants of the tail, within two weeks.

The spadefoots, therefore, have circumvented the need for permanent pools. Owing to the extraordinarily long tadpole stage, the bullfrog, in contrast, is as securely tied to the water as the mudpuppies, *Necturus*, or the hellbender, *Cryptobranchus*, and a few other salamanders that never lose their gills and seldom leave the water unless forced to. Several of the aquatic salamanders, dubbed "permanent larvae," reach maturity in the sense that they can breed, despite their retention of gills and other juvenile traits.

The hellbender, which may attain a length of 27 inches, may be the heaviest salamander in the United States. It is exceeded in length, however, by an inhabitant of the Gulf Coast swamps, a slender-bodied, vestigial-limbed salamander called the two-toed amphiuma

The red-spotted newt is an aquatic salamander that seldom, if ever, leaves water

or Congo eel, *Amphiuma means*, that reaches 40 inches in length. The only salamanders outside the United States that approach this maximum, also exceed it. These are both relatives of the hellbender, the giant salamanders (*Andrias* – long known as *Megalobatrachus*), of China and Japan.

The Japanese giant salamander, *Andrias japonicus*, weighs as much as 90 pounds, and attains a length of nearly five feet. It exceeds all living amphibians in weight, but its length is equaled by one of the eel-shaped caecilians that inhabit tropical South America. Similarly, the American bullfrog is outclassed by two South American toads, each of which reaches nine inches in length. An Asiatic toad may prove to be still larger, but in length all of them are surpassed by the twelve-inch body of the West African frog that was appropriately called *Rana goliath*.

Longevity

Marking experiments suggest that it is not unusual for some amphibians to live four or five years, or even longer. Bullfrogs may live longer than ten years but as we have seen, relatively few reach maturity. Adult individuals in populations of some of the least secretive species that have been studied appear to be largely replaced every three or four years. Nevertheless, a toad with a life expectancy of four or five years in its natural habitat is potentially capable of living much longer. Under captive conditions one European toad allegedly survived for 40 years. The giant salamanders not only hold the record for size, but for longevity as well. Perhaps because they are not difficult to keep in aquaria, at least six individuals are said to have attained ages between 50 and 60 years. Other large salamanders, particularly the aquatic species that retain their gills, have lived for a quarter of a century in captivity.

Protective Devices and Predators

The avoidance of predators is a lifelong preoccupation of amphibians. Every group of backboned animals, from fishes to mammals, contains species that prey on amphibians. Also, many amphibians are not averse to preying on one another. Predatory fishes large enough, and seemingly eager to devour all but the largest amphibians, are prevalent in rivers, ponds, and lakes. Frogs sometimes behave as though they were aware of this. Leopard frogs, *Rana pipiens*, approached along the banks of a river in Mexico could not be induced to leap into the water. The reason became apparent when a frog that inadvertently fell into the river was promptly seized by a large fish. Frogs of the same species living along a brook a few miles away readily leaped into pools that contained only small fishes.

Leaping, it may be noted,is something more than a means of progression. Frogs often escape the jaws of predators by abruptly rocketing the body beyond their reach. Not many amphibians are large enough to be aggressive, although a hellbender, equipped as it is with teeth, can inflict a painful bite. Such tactics would be useless to the smaller amphibians, which are more often agile and able to flee from a predator or to seek cover. Slippery skins may be less effective than the poisons that exude from the skins. Toads and forest frogs (those of the family Dendrobatidae) in particular, are well supplied with poison glands. Indians used the secretions on the skins of one or more of the forest frogs in Colombia and Panama to poison their arrows. The extremely potent poison on the skins of the Pacific newts (*Taricha*) discourages attacks by some carnivores that eat other salamanders.

Inasmuch as most amphibians are abroad and active at night they escape the attention of many, but by no means all of the diurnal predators. Numerous nocturnal animals including skunks, bobcats, coyotes, and especially raccoons, prey on frogs, as do some owls. Such limbless reptiles as the tiny ringneck snakes (*Diadophis*) devour salamanders, and the hognose snakes (*Heterodon*) habitually prey on toads. Amphibians seemingly find it difficult to detect, and hence also to avoid, the stealthy approach of snakes, otherwise amphibians would not so commonly terminate their lives in snake stomachs. Caecilians fit neatly into the digestive tracts of snakes, and that is precisely where some have been found.

Amphibians are patterned or colored in ways that afford protection from some predators. The gaudy reds and yellows of several frogs and salamanders that secrete poisons have been interpreted as "warning coloration." The patterns or colors of other frogs and salamanders tend to conceal them in their natural environments. The markings of the Appalachian green salamander, *Aneides aeneus*, for example, closely resemble the lichens on the cliffs it inhabits. The coloration of canyon tree frogs, *Hyla arenicolor*, in Arizona and New Mexico harmonizes with the boulders on which they rest during the day. Bold patterns tend to disrupt the continuity on the surface and hence also the body outlines of many amphibians. On a unicolored surface the large-blotched salamander, *Ensatina eschscholtzi klauberi*, of California is conspicuous. At night in the shadows of the litter on the forest floor where it forages, however, the bright orange and black blotches blend with the background. In effect, the contours of the body are obliterated in the shadows.

A bark-colored tree frog clinging to a

The tiger salamander is equally at home in water, or a moist, terrestrial habitat

tree trunk or the green-colored frog resting on a leaf are easily overlooked by animals that detect their prey largely by means of vision. Owing to their slothful locomotion, salamanders are nearly as inconspicuous as immobile objects. Faster movements alert both prey and predator, but extremely fast movements can be advantageous. Few predators are able to follow the movements of a leaping tree frog. Its abrupt departure often leaves the predator not only out on a limb but on the wrong limb. The frog may land on a twig or branch outside the predator's range of vision.

Unfortunately for amphibians, they fall prey to numerous animals that depend less upon vision than other senses. The majority of the snakes detect or even trail their prey by means of an acute sense of smell. A few snakes rely heavily on visual cues, but most of them employ both smell and vision as they slowly and noiselessly approach their prey. Most often the caecilian, frog, or salamander has been seized before it was aware of the snake's presence. Without much doubt, snakes are among the most successful and ubiquitous of the predators that plague amphibians. Pages would be required, however, to list all the other backboned animals that devour amphibians at some stage in their lives.

Amphibians, such as this American toad, feed on small animals such as earthworms

The parasites of amphibians seldom kill them outright, but some may shorten their hosts' lives. Bacteria, roundworms, flatworms, mites, ticks, and countless other parasites infest amphibians. Quite possibly, however, the activities of human beings in many areas are at least as detrimental as those of parasites. Vehicles flatten millions of frogs and toads and thousands of salamanders annually, especially in areas where routes of migration cross highways. The damage inflicted on amphibian populations by automobiles and trucks is minor, however, compared to what frogs and salamanders have suffered from insecticides.

Careless, not to say misguided, spraying of lakes, ponds, and swamps often leaves hordes of dead amphibians. Years may be required before some populations return to normal levels – as they may if a sufficiently large number survive. Populations never recover, however, when their habitats have been ruined, as so many have been. The pollution of streams, and the drainage of swamps will inevitably exterminate many more amphibian populations. In some instances the water pumped to the surface in areas being exploited agriculturally has attracted frogs or toads. These additions to the terrain a few frogs can inhabit, however, scarcely counterbalance the losses that amphibians suffer as a direct result of man's destruction of many of their natural habitats.

Food and Feeding Habits

An exceptionally large bullfrog, *Rana catesbeiana*, can devour a hatchling alligator. This seldom happens. An alligator of moderate dimensions easily crushes and swallows an adult bullfrog, and this often happens. Relatively few kinds of animals that a bullfrog eats become large enough later in life to eat a bullfrog. In this exceptional instance, the size of the hatchling was the criterion. Whether an amphibian has teeth, or lacks them, it swallows its prey whole. Consequently amphibians invariably prey on animals smaller than themselves. The offspring of its larger predators can become the prey of the bullfrog only when they are approximately the size of the other small animals that a bullfrog eats.

Size is often reflected in the sequence of predators that food-chains illustrate. An American satirist named Ambrose Bierce offered an example of food-chain before the term had been coined when he defined the word *edible*, as "Good to eat, and wholesome to digest, as a worm to a toad, a toad to a snake, a snake to a pig, a pig to a man, and a man to a worm." Amphibians are commonly the second link in the chain, not because they live wholly on worms, but because their diet consists largely of the *key industry animals.* In addition to earthworms, these include snails, slugs, sow bugs, millipedes, and insects in particular. Such animals are the primary consumers that either feed on plants, or derive their food from vegetable products. When amphibians eat scorpions and spiders that prey upon insects, they become secondary consumers and advance one link in the chain. Were they to feed exclusively upon scavengers, however, they would drop back one link.

Directly or indirectly, all food is derived from the energy that plants store. Food-chains greatly oversimplify the situation, if only because few animals restrict their diet to one kind of animal. All amphibians are carnivorous, but not many of them are specialists. The nar-

The American toad's tongue has lightning action for snapping up insects

The pickerel frog (above) resembles the leopard frog, but has squarish spots

row-mouthed toads (*Gastrophryne*) and the sheep frog (*Hypopachus*) of the United States apparently subsist largely on ants. But the diet of the more widely distributed green frog, *Rana clamitans*, is far more varied. One study revealed that insects comprised 76 percent of its food, the remainder of which consisted of spiders, molluscs, crustaceans, millipedes, centipedes, earthworms, and fishes. Green frogs had also eaten their own cast skins, a habit they share with other amphibians.

The same groups of animals were represented in the diet of the American toad, *Bufo americanus*, which forages farther from water than the green frog. The toad had not eaten the same kinds of insects, but they comprised 77 percent of its diet. The volume of millipedes the toad consumed was five times greater than that of the frog. Ants and beetles are prominent in the diets of many toads. In fact, the giant toad, *Bufo marinus*, a native of the American tropics with a distribution that extends to southern Texas, is believed to be one of the few predators effective in controlling the beetles that infest sugar cane. Cane growers have found it worthwhile to introduce this large toad into Australia and many other areas where cane is grown.

Mudpuppies (*Necturus*) and newts (*Notophthalmus*) have been incriminated as devourers of fish eggs, but their damage to fish populations is insignificant. The Surinam toad, *Pipa pipa*, however, is one of the few amphibians that habitually eats fishes. It is distantly related to the toads, contrary to inferences that might be drawn from the vernacular name. Any toad attracted by the movements of a small arthropod waits until it is close enough to snare its prey and draw it into the mouth on the end of its sticky tongue. Most other terrestrial amphibians employ much the same procedure, but not the Surinam toad.

Tongues cannot be used to snare prey in the water. This explains why the Surinam toad and its relatives in South America and the clawed toads (*Xenopus*) of Africa are tongueless. Only the Surinam toad, however, is provided with a lure, a wormlike structure that extends below the snout. This flat, unobtrusive amphibian sits on the bottom of pools, waiting with the digits on its forefeet distended in front of the mouth. Any small fish that approaches the lure is detected the moment it touches the distended digits, and the Surinam toad

The dark-sided salamander usually lives in the twilight zone of caverns

Fowler's toad

sects eaten by clawed toads in Africa have apparently fallen into the ponds. Any of the tongueless toads would presumably be ill-equipped to seize its prey on land.

To some extent availability determines what any amphibian eats. Creatures too large to pass through an amphibian's mouth, however, automatically become unavailable. Large frogs apparently ignore extremely small animals that are eaten by proportionately smaller amphibians. The size of the prey is more closely associated with the size attained by the species, however, than with the size

Spotted salamander

lurches forward and quickly engulfs it.

Teeth on the jaws of salamanders, caecilians, and some frogs, enable them to grasp and subdue their prey. The forelimbs may or may not be used to force the morsel into the mouth. Whenever toads, all of them toothless, manage to snare any animal that does not readily fit into the mouth, however, their forelimbs invariably hasten the operation.

As might be anticipated, the prey of aquatic amphibians consists mostly of animals that live in the water. Adult Surinam toads in British Guiana eat armored catfishes. The few terrestial in-

Wood frog

of the individual. Before a frog is fully adult in size, its diet differs little from that of much larger frogs of the same species.

Amphibians, as secondary consumers, provide food for a host of other animals, including man. The traffic in frog legs in unimportant in the economy of most nations. Where man has exterminated larger game, however, amphibians assume more importance as a source of protein. So little meat is obtainable in parts of North America that the natives eat frog tadpoles. In the United States, however, more amphibians are sold to laboratories than to meat markets.

Amphibians and Man

Human beings have been resourceful, if not always enlightened, in their efforts to exploit amphibians. We can safely assume today that toads go into the witch's brew only in Shakespearean plays and the cartoons of Charles Addams. These and other tailless amphibians, however, still become ingredients of "antidotes" prescribed by practitioners of primitive medicine. In Mexico the Tarascan Indians market the *achoque*, a salamander (*Bathysiredon*, restricted to the waters of Lake Patzcuaro), as a suitable remedy for diseases of the chest. Elsewhere the skins of frogs not only afford a source of poison, but also a source of leather for coin purses, surely an ignominious end for some of the large toads. In the United States salamanders are sold as fish bait in some areas.

Where frogs or toads are abundant they consume many insects that gardeners regard as pests. Not all insects are injurious to plants or animals, but the pests commonly outnumber harmless insects in the diets of toads living in truck gardens and cane fields. If other amphibians are not considered beneficial, few of them are looked upon as being harmful. Through human carelessness salamanders may occasionally contaminate water supplies when latrines or outhouses are built near reservoirs. Nevertheless, frogs or salamanders rarely harbor parasites or diseases that plague human beings. Land owners are generally and properly irate when strong chemical insecticides, applied for nuisance insect control, leave the margins of ponds strewn with dead frogs. Is it not better to tolerate a few mosquitoes rather than lose the magic voice of the spring peeper, *Hyla crucifer*?

More significant but less tangible benefits to mankind have been derived from the wide use of amphibians in biological and medical investigations. Frogs are now more widely used than other animals in pregnancy tests. More important, perhaps, much of our knowledge of the medically important ductless glands and the effects of various hormones is traceable to investigations that dealt with amphibians. Few animals have been more profitably studied than these creatures whose ancestors bridged the gaps between gills and lungs and between fins and limbs. —C.M.B.

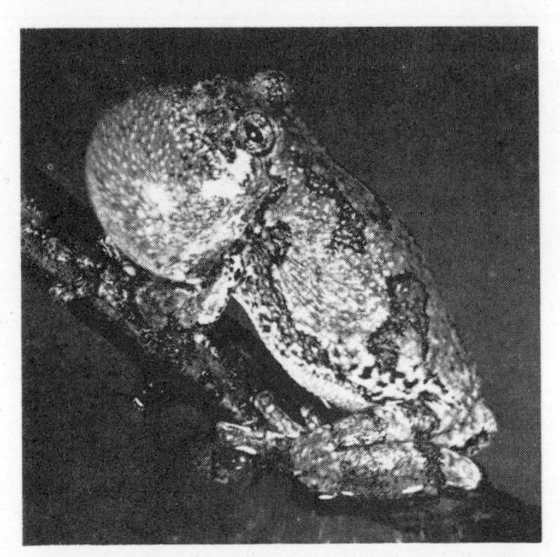

The tree frog, or tree toad, is an arboreal animal that has a distinctive call

Recommended Reading

A Field Guide to Reptiles and Amphibians—Roger Conant. Houghton Mifflin Co., Boston.

Handbook of Frogs and Toads—A. A. Wright, and A. H. Wright. Third edition. Comstock Publishing Co., Ithaca, New York.

Handbook of Salamanders—Sherman C. Bishop. Hafner Publishing Company, New York.

Rue anemone

ANEMONE

Rue Anemone
Other Common Names—Windflower, mayflower
Scientific Name—*Anemonella thalictroides*
Family—Ranunculaceae (crowfoot family)
Range—Eastern North America, south to Florida
Habitat—Rich woodlands
Time of Blooming—March through June

The delicate rue anemone blooms in the early spring. It has several white or pinkish flowers on slender stalks, and compound leaves that are elevated on the stem.

The showy parts of the flowers are the sepals since there are no petals. Usually there are three blossoms that open gradually from the center outward as the stamens and pistils mature. This prolongs the blooming season of the rue and encourages cross-pollination by insects.

The whole plant seldom reaches a height of more than nine inches. As the stem is slender but sturdy, the wind tosses it about freely; hence its other name, windflower.

Rue anemone is often placed in a genus by itself, *Anemonella,* that means somewhat like anemone. Its leaves resemble the rues which also have no petals.

It grows only in woodlands that are rich in humus and is most plentiful in deciduous forests. Here the plant can obtain sufficient sunlight to complete its blooming period before the leaves of the trees expand and shade it. The plant winters as an underground bulb, having stored food for nourishment during the early spring growth.

Wood Anemone
Other Common Names—Windflower
Scientific Name—*Anemone quinquefolia*
Family—Ranunculaceae (crowfoot family)
Range—Quebec to North Carolina and western New York, locally in Ohio and Kentucky
Habitat—Edges of woods
Time of Blooming—April through June

The wood anemone is a delicate spring flower which commonly grows along the edge of the woods. It stands four to nine inches high and bears a single white, sometimes pinkish, flower about one inch across at the top of a slender stalk.

Its slender stem grows from an elongated rootstock; part way up the stem are a pair of deeply divided leaves. These have three main divisions which often appear to be five; hence the specific name *quinquefolia* (five-leaved).

The generic name *Anemone* is a corruption of *Na man*, the Semitic name for Adonis, from whose blood the crimson-flowered anemone of the Orient is said to have sprung.

The flower has no petals, but its four to nine sepals are petal-like. The flowers are polinated by early season bees and the beelike flies (*Bombylius*). Like others of this genus the wood anemone is a perennial. It has a whitish, toothed, underground stem which extends horizontally beneath the surface.

Both the wood anemone and the rue anemone are members of the crowfoot family. This species can be identified by its narrow leaves with branching segments. There are numerous other anemones that grow in damp thickets and meadows.

In the past some types of anemones were used as medicinals. At one time they were prescribed for ills associated with the eyes and teeth. They were also administered as an herbal to those given to excesses of emotion. (*See also Wild Flower*) —A.M.M.

Wood anemone

ANEMONE (*See under Sea Anemone*)

ANGIOSPERM (*See under Tree; Plant Kingdom*)

ANHINGA

Other Common Names—Water turkey, snakebird

Scientific Name—*Anhinga anhinga*

Family—Anhingidae (darters)

Order—Pelecaniformes

Size—Length, 34 to 36 inches

Range—Tropical and warm temperate parts of North and South America, north to North Carolina, southern Illinois and Arkansas, and south to Argentina

This strange, almost prehistoric-looking bird is a slender relative of the cormorant, and except for its near absence from salt water, is often mistaken for that other blackish waterbird, the cormorant.

The anhinga's plumage is thick and compact—almost furry. It is glossy greenish-black, but the wing coverts are pale gray, the tail tipped with brown. The female's head, neck, and breast are a grayish-buff, otherwise she resembles the male.

Anhingas are freshwater birds, living in marshy sloughs, rivers, or bayous, and on ponds bordered by bushes or small trees. There the anhingas spend most of their time, sitting in small groups in low trees or bushes, occasionally holding their wings outspread to the sun. On a perch the anhinga is rather clumsy, but once in the air it is a graceful bird and a strong flier, and often soars to considerable heights.

The alternate flapping and sailing, together with the very slender head and neck and the long, broad tail, make the

The anhinga is sometimes called water turkey, or snakebird

anhinga easy to distinguish, even at a distance. When frightened from its perch, it will sometimes drop like an arrow into the water, and when it reappears, only the slender, snakelike neck shows above the surface. Like a cormorant, its bones are heavy, and it can submerge without a ripple. It does not, as a rule, plunge for its prey, but instead dives from the surface and swims under water.

The anhinga feeds almost exclusively on fishes, including several species that man himself covets, but these are practically all taken in swamps where commercial fishing is seldom practiced.

Its nest, solidly built of twigs, often with some Spanish moss, and lined with green leaves or small twigs, is placed in the upright fork of a bush or tree, 5 to 100 feet above the ground. The chalky-white eggs number three to six in a clutch, and are usually laid from the first of March to the middle of May, although eggs have been found as late as July.

ANI

Smooth-billed Ani

Other Common Names—Parrot blackbird, black witch, tickbird, Cuban parrot

Scientific Name—*Crotophaga ani*

Family—Cuculidae (cuckoos, roadrunners, and anis)

Order—Cuculiformes

Size—Length, 13 to 15 inches

Range—Eastern South America and the West Indies; also locally in Louisiana and southern Florida

With its somber coal-black plumage, strange appearance, and awkward movements, the ani is always an object of curiosity and interest even to the casual observer.

Superficially and at a distance the ani may resemble the boat-tailed grackle, as both are black and of approximately the same size. The flight patterns of the two are somewhat alike, but here all similarity ends, as the personality, movements in the trees, beaks, calls, and feeding habits of the two vary greatly.

The groove-billed ani, *Crotophaga sulcirostris,* is similar in appearance to the smooth-billed, but the grooves on the bill of this species can easily be observed. The groove-billed ani nests from the lower Rio Grande Valley, Texas, south to Peru and is occasionally seen in Arizona, Kansas, Louisiana, and Florida.

The nest of the smooth-billed ani is bulky, built of sticks, weeds, leaves, and grass, usually at a low elevation, in tangles of vines or in small trees. The eggs are greenish-blue, with a chalky deposit. Five to seven are laid each season. The season varies widely, and eggs have been found in March, early June, mid-July, and late September.

Although suffering from the predations of small boys and from periodic clean-up campaigns, a small colony of smooth-billed anis near Clewiston, Florida, has been maintaining itself. The increasing number of observers who visit this location specifically to see the anis has helped arouse interest on the part of the civic authorities in protecting them as a municipal asset.

The smooth-billed ani

ANIMAL

Animal Habitats of a Forest

A forest is a community of living things. One is accustomed to the idea of a community, for each person is a member of one community or another. People are members of a community because of where they live as, for example, in a city, village, apartment house, or hotel. They are also members of a community because of their interrelated activity, whether in schools, offices, or factories. A forest is a community because of the plants or animals that live there and because of their interrelated activities. In fact, the relationships of life in a forest may be compared to the relations within a community of human beings, and there will be many apparent similarities.

The Forest as a Hotel

To simplify the comparison, however, one should consider the similarities between a forest and a hotel, rather than between a forest and an entire city community. Both a forest and a hotel have different layers or floors, with some individuals living on certain floors, and others moving from floor to floor.

The large metropolitan hotel has many floors. Similarly, a large mature forest has many different layers formed by plants. For example, in the eastern deciduous forest one layer is made of flowers and herbs rising from the forest floor. Other layers are: a shrub layer, a layer formed by leaves of small trees, and a canopy layer, formed high overhead by the leaves of the tallest trees.

A young forest, or a second growth or cut-over forest, may have only an herbaceous layer and a small tree layer. Perhaps a young forest may be compared to a motel of one or two floors.

Life in the Forest Basement

Important parts of any hotel are the foundation and the basement. The counterpart of the hotel basement in a forest is the soil layer, and the foundations of the forest are the plant roots that extend through the soil.

Raw materials present in the soil are taken up through roots to higher layers, much as in a hotel, where water, electricity, and gas pass from the basement through pipes and cables to the floors above. Down to the basement comes the refuse to be disposed of. In the forest, broken twigs, leaves, flower petals, and many other plant and animal remains and waste products reach the soil from the upper levels. As this material reaches the soil it is decomposed by a host of small forms including bacteria, fungi, algae, earthworms, roundworms, termites, protozoans, and many others. These organisms utilize the refuse material in their own energy systems. Through the resulting chemical and mechanical changes in the material it is reduced to a state again usable by the green plants of the community.

Other small soil inhabitants include mites, springtails, snails, millipedes, insect larvae, moles, and some predacious forms like shrews, centipedes, spiders, and ground beetles which feed on the other basement dwellers. In addition, the forest soil serves as a refuge during the winter for species of salamanders, toads, lizards, snakes, the striped skunk, and woodchuck, all of which remain more or less inactive during the colder weather.

The Busy Forest Floor

The most familiar area of a hotel is the first floor or lobby. This is also the busiest place in the building, for here pass all those going to higher or lower floors. Visitors rest in the lobby, and convention delegates greet one another there. The lobby of the forest is the surface of the ground, with its tree-to-tree carpeting of leaf litter.

Deer, rabbits, white-footed mice, chipmunks, woodchucks, weasels, skunks, raccoons, and gray foxes make use of the lobby, though some of these may visit other floors. For example, the skunk pokes about the forest floor but hibernates in the ground. The raccoon ambles about over the floor yet has a den or two in trees. White-footed mice probably spend most of their time on the forest floor, but may nest in logs, stumps, burrows, and even in old bird nests in bushes and small trees.

Most of the small mammals of the forest floor (weasels, moles and voles, shrews, chipmunks) take advantage of tunnels and burrows leading into the ground for shelter. Ovenbirds nest and feed on the forest floor. Likewise, many species of warblers nest on the ground, though they feed and sing from higher layers in the forest.

Life Under the Forest Carpet

Unlike a tidy hotel, there are many animals under the carpet of leaf litter in a forest lobby. These may be slugs, snails, scarab beetles, ground beetles, burying beetles, carrion beetles, spiders, shrews, voles, sowbugs, crickets, and a long list of others. Some of these may move into the ground from time to time, but they are rarely seen unless one looks carefully under logs, stones, or the leaf litter covering the ground.

Dwellers from higher up may visit the forest floor, as when a titmouse or a chickadee drops down to pick up a particularly fine morsel of food. The most common transients are insects, but the forest floor may be used by residents of all layers. A convention of ants usually can be observed on the forest floor, but the real business, the tending of eggs and larvae, goes on in the soil below. Many residents of the forest floor reduce leaf litter to humus, and others work on and in stumps and fall-

A cross-section of a forest reveals the stratification of its vegetation

Canopy—*A young bald eagle watches the forest from its treetop nest of twigs*

Understory—*A hummingbird nests in a small elm tree beneath forest canopy*

Shrub layer—*Nesting in a viburnum, a hooded warbler incubates its eggs*

Forest floor—*The eastern woodchuck forages among the herbs of the forest floor*

Basement—*The eastern mole burrows beneath the forest in search of insects*

A typical resident of each layer in the stratification of a forest is shown above

en logs. Many kinds of molds, fungi, bacteria, snails, mites, carpenter ants, and others are engaged in these activities.

Layer of Forest Flowers

Above the lobby in most hotels is a mezzanine. This is usually an incomplete floor and may be used only part of the year for conventions and the like. The herbaceous layer of the forest may be compared to the mezzanine. Grasses and flowering herbs occur in patches through the forest, though they may be very sparse in a mature forest. The herbaceous layer changes with the seasons. During the winter this layer hardly exists. In the spring, may-apple, jack-in-the-pulpit, false lily of the valley, trillium and the like may form an almost continuous layer. In the summer, when the dense growth of tree leaves forms a closed canopy over the forest, much of the herbaceous layer is shaded out and becomes inconspicuous.

A few birds may occasionally nest in the herbaceous layer (Kentucky warbler, for instance), and birds may glean insects from the leaves of plants. Leafhoppers are frequent, and spring peepers may call from this herbaceous undergrowth.

Forest Shrub Layer

Above the mezzanine are the residential floors of the hotel. The first of these in the forest is the layer formed by shrubs growing from four to eight feet high. In the East this layer may include maple-leaved viburnum, spicebush, blueberry, and other shrubs, plus tree seedlings and saplings, and vines. As the shrub layer is the level of the forest closest to our hands and eyes, a little observation will introduce one to many animals feeding on the leaves of these plants. Leaf miners, leaf and treehoppers, aphids, tent caterpillars, and many other insects can be observed. Nesting birds of the shrub layer may include towhee, catbird, cuckoo, cardinal, wood thrush, Swainson's warbler, and hooded warbler. In addition, these and other birds use the shrub layer for refuge from predators and for song perches.

As people are not expected to stay always on the same floor in a hotel, so one does not expect species and individuals of animals to be found always in the same layer of the forest. Many of the birds named above as typical of the shrub layer, will occasionally nest on the ground or up in a small tree, and any of them may occasionally be found high in the canopy of the forest.

The towhee, for example, frequently nests on the ground, as well as in shrubs and small trees in brushy openings in the forest. Yet it often feeds on the ground, and may sing from the tops of small trees. Various species of insects, including mirid bugs, aphids, leaf miners, leaf rollers, gall insects, beetles, and flies show distributions centered in certain layers but do extend to layers above and below. Parasites and predators of these animals distribute themselves according to the location of their prey, but are not specifically restricted to one layer.

On the Stairs—Forest Tree Trunks

In a hotel people pass from floor to floor using stairways or elevators. In a forest there are no elevators, but tree trunks serve well as stairways. Squirrels may be conspicuous as they race up and down tree trunks. Black and white, warblers, nuthatches, creepers, and woodpeckers are noticeable users of the forest stairs. The tree trunks form a type of vertical layer, with many inhabitants—darkling beetles, wood boring beetles, click beetles, and crevice or hole nesting birds like brown creepers, woodpeckers, titmice, chickadees, crested flycatchers, and owls. Incidentally, tree trunks form an important area where insects may overwinter as eggs, immature or adult forms, and provide winter food for woodpeckers and nuthatches.

Small Tree Layer

The middle floors of a hotel seem to have considerable use. Plenty of rooms are available at a reasonable cost. In a forest small trees make up a definite understory. Together with a taller subcanopy layer, they make up the middle and upper floors of the forest hotel. The understory is usually formed of such trees as dogwood, cherry, and hornbeam. Young or stunted oaks, maples, and hickories make up the subcanopy. Typical residents of this layer include the red-eyed vireo, redstart, and Acadian flycatcher.

Red-eyed vireo

More birds sing from the small trees and tall shrubs of the understory than from any other layer of the forest. Even the ovenbird, though a ground nester, consistently sings from this layer. Most birds of the lower layers, when disturbed, fly up to the refuge offered by the understory, and almost all species may be found there at one time or another. Less is known of smaller and inconspicuous animals of the understory, primarily because we do not often visit these higher floors of the forest.

Top Floor—Forest Canopy

If little is known about the upper floors of a hotel, even less is known about life up in the penthouse. Few persons are ever invited there and if one goes he usually does not stay long. The penthouse of the forest is the canopy. Like tycoons in their penthouses, the trees forming the canopy are dominants.

The leaves of the tallest oaks, beech, sugar maple, basswoods, and hickories intercept most of the sun's rays that fall on the forest, and this means they receive most of the energy. Lesser amounts of sun energy are used and stored in understory and shrub layers. All herbivorous animals utilize a part of this energy stored in plants. Because of the canopy the lower layers are cooler in summer and much less disturbed by wind; humidity is higher than in open fields.

The number of plants that can thrive under the shade of the canopy of summer is limited. In fact, the presence of the high canopy and its effect on light, precipitation, temperature, wind, and humidity, creates many of the conditions responsible for the layered growth in the forest. Typical animals of the forest canopy include cicadas, scarlet tanagers, hawks, owls, Baltimore orioles, Blackburnian warblers, and many others.

Where one stays in a hotel depends on the number of rooms and how much they cost. Where animals live in the forest depends greatly on where their food is most abundant, but other factors are important. For example, distribution of birds may be determined not only by location of food, but also by availability of nest sites and location of singing perches in the forest.

One consequence of layering in forests is that a great variety of niches (microhabitats) are available. This means that more animals are able to maintain themselves over a given area of land than might otherwise be possible. This same general plan exists in tall skyscraper

The chipmunk, an able tree climber, spends most of its time on the forest floor

hotels, where many floors stacked one on the other permit accommodation of a larger number of people than would a one-story ranch house occupying the same area of land. In the winter the strata formed by leaves of trees, shrubs, and flowers disappear, though the limbs, trunks, and stems of trees and shrubs remain, and in the open crowns of winter trees will be nests of squirrels.

To think of a forest as a hotel is a useful concept and serves to introduce the subject that botanists call *stratification.* The layers or floors of the forest are called *strata* (singular is *stratum*). A scientist speaks of the shrub *stratum* rather than of the shrub *layer.* No matter what names one uses more information is needed on the layers (strata) of the forest, particularly the higher layers. What animals live there, in what strata do they spend their time and what do they do? What are the limits of life for each layer of the forest? There is an opportunity for the amateur, as well as the professional naturalist to add to existing information. —J.S.

Recommended Reading

The Forest and the Sea—Marston Bates. Random House, New York.

Fundamentals of Ecology—Eugene P. Odum. W. B. Saunders Company, Philadelphia.

The Living Forest—Jack McCormick. Harper and Brothers, New York.

The Tale of a Wood—Henry B. Kane. Knopf, New York.

The Web of Nature—Theodore S. Pettit. Garden City Books, Garden City, New York.

Woodland Ecology—Ernest Neal. Harvard University Press, Cambridge, Massachusetts.

Animal Tracks

When the sun sets and the twilight deepens, a wave of activity spreads through the animal world. Although there may have been some travel through the mouse tunnels in the grass by day and a few rabbits seen in the meadows, it is not until dusk brings its protecting cover that the animals of the countryside venture forth in numbers.

Then, from east, west, north, and south across the continent, from out of burrows in the ground and hollows in trees, from crevices in rocks, from under bark, old logs, and other shelter according to locality, come shrews, muskrats, beavers, pocket mice, grasshopper mice, kangaroo rats, pack rats, flying squirrels, rabbits, meadow mice, and white-footed mice—to mention only a few. Under cover of darkness they set about their nightly business of eating; some to chew the plant roots and young grass shoots; some to gnaw the bark, to nibble seeds or to collect and store them; some to capture insects, cold and sluggish in the cool grass and old leaves.

But although the dark shadows afford a measure of protection, danger lurks everywhere for these small, more or less defenseless creatures. With such a feast of little plant and insect eaters abroad, other larger animals keep ears alert for every squeak, listening for the slightest sound of scurrying feet. The birds and beasts of prey—owls, skunks, raccoons, weasels, and mink—are on the hunt searching for a mouse, a muskrat, or shrew. Still bigger ears are listening too, not only for a mouse's squeak but for the tread of the hunting weasel and the mink. These ears belong to the larger carnivores—the fox, bobcat, and great horned owl.

In passing through the countryside by day, few persons would suspect the multitudes of animals residing there. Even if one stepped out into the night, there would be little to indicate the struggles for food taking place perhaps only a few feet away. Lacking the eyes

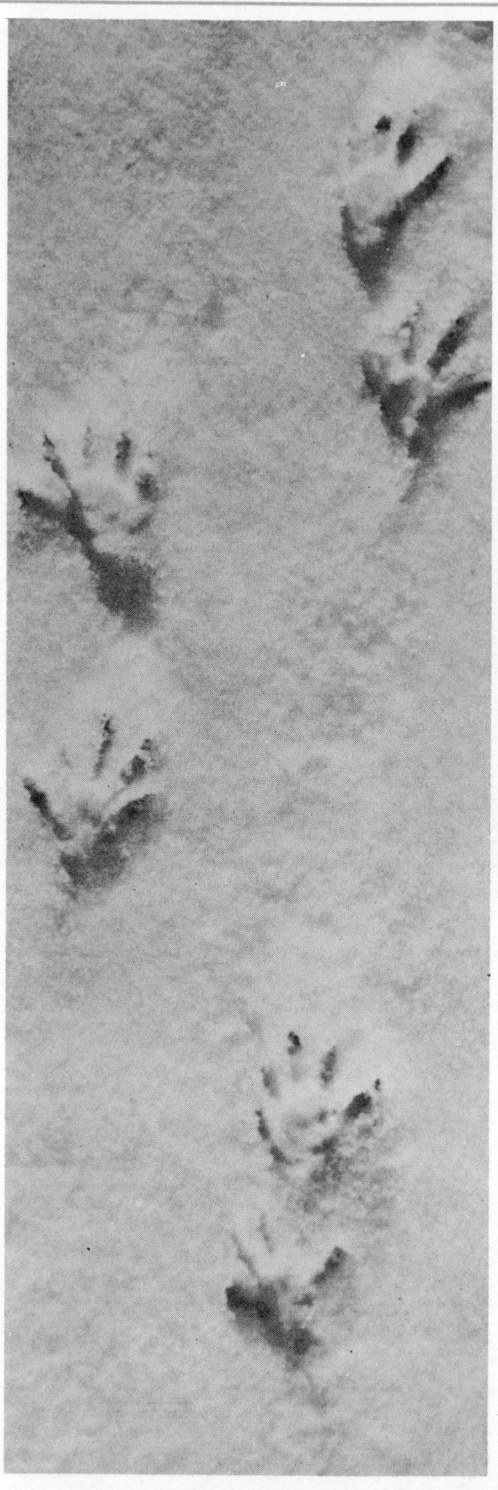

A raccoon leaves its tracks in snow

and ears of the cat or owl, it seems impossible for most would-be observers to witness these dramatic episodes. Yet there are ways of finding out who these shy neighbors are, and even of ascertaining their activities. For example, it can be discerned that during the night a great-horned owl captured a weasel that had just eaten a field mouse caught while nibbling grass roots in the pasture. There are ways of learning something about the hundreds of other similar chain dinners devoured every night, with each participant in turn a prey for another, each fitting inside the one next larger, like a nest of children's blocks.

Fortunately, for the curious, clues to the night's food dramas are frequently left behind in the footprints and track patterns of the actors. Should one find what looks to be the print of a baby's foot in a muddy bank by the stream, it probably means that a skunk has passed there; the print of a forefoot with long toes spreading like fingers of a tiny hand is the mark of a raccoon; two large bird tracks may show where a heron stood motionless, perhaps at dawn, waiting for some unwary frog to come along; that curious wide trail flanked with tiny footprints with here and there a short curving line in the center shows where a turtle passed and dragged its tail.

On a stretch of sandy beach are fascinating patterns made by hundreds of sandpiper toes; there are the prints of gulls' feet, ducks' feet, and bands of dots where the many-footed crab ran sideways; a curved path made by the single-footed clam. All of these marks, like signatures in a hotel register, tell who has come and gone. But it is in winter on smooth sheets of new snow that complete recordings of animal food hunting are shown.

Hands, feet, claws, tails are the "pens" that write these stories. For each kind of animal these marks are distinctive. The arrangement of the prints of hind feet and forefeet is typical of the animal too and also indicates the

A snake's track meanders through sand

A grizzly bear's tracks left in mud

gait and speed—whether walking, running, crawling, hopping, or galloping.

Animals that Bound

Mice, rats, squirrels, and rabbits travel by bounding, a sort of gallop. The prints of all four feet are made with each bound and in every case the prints of the two hind feet are side by side (paired) and in front of the marks made by the forefeet. Thus, paradoxical as it may seem, in the track patterns of mice, squirrels, and rabbits, the hind footprints lead in the direction the animal was going. Close examination of the tracks to see the toe marks will bear out

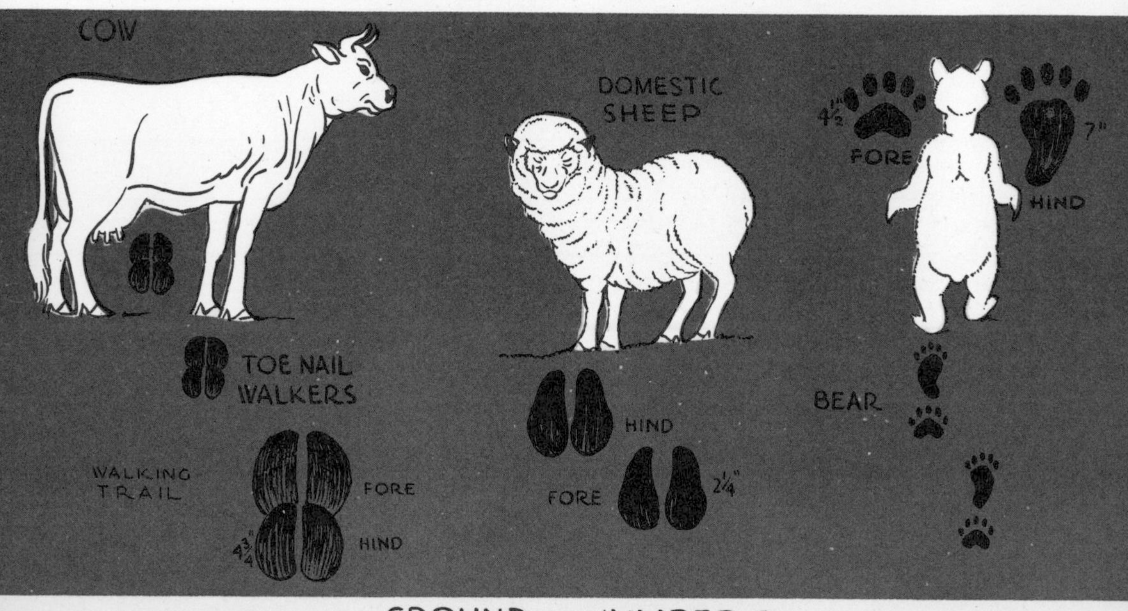

GROUND JUMPERS

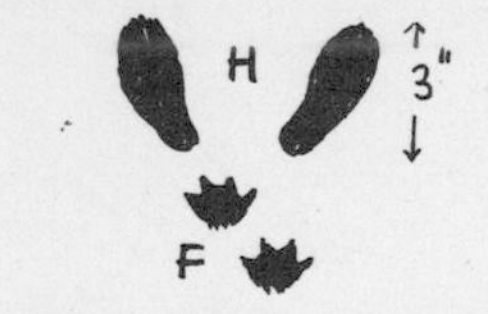

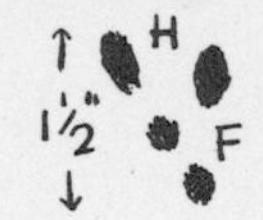

COTTONTAIL RABBIT FIELD MOUSE CHIPMUNK

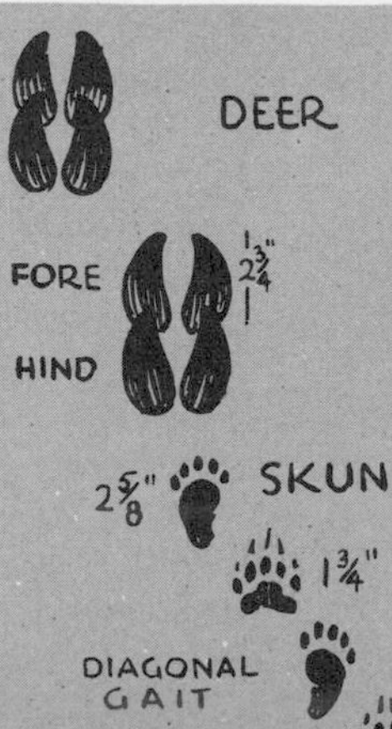

TOE WALKER

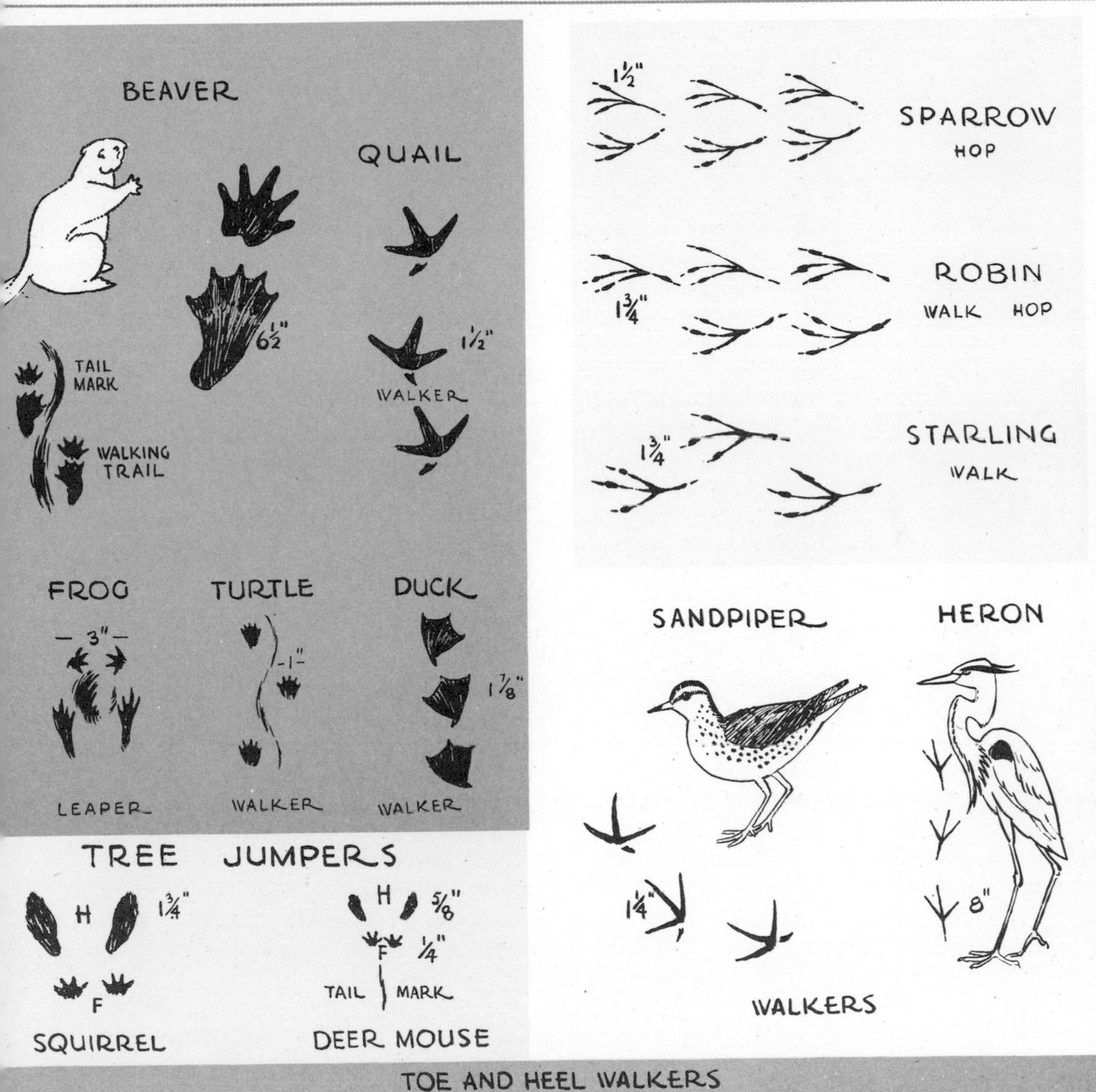
BEAVER
TAIL MARK
WALKING TRAIL
6½"
QUAIL
1½"
WALKER
FROG
— 3" —
LEAPER
TURTLE
-1"
WALKER
DUCK
1⅞"
WALKER
TREE JUMPERS
H
1¾"
F
SQUIRREL
H
⅝"
F
¼"
TAIL MARK
DEER MOUSE
1½"
SPARROW
HOP
1¾"
ROBIN
WALK HOP
1¾"
STARLING
WALK
SANDPIPER
1¼"
HERON
8"
WALKERS

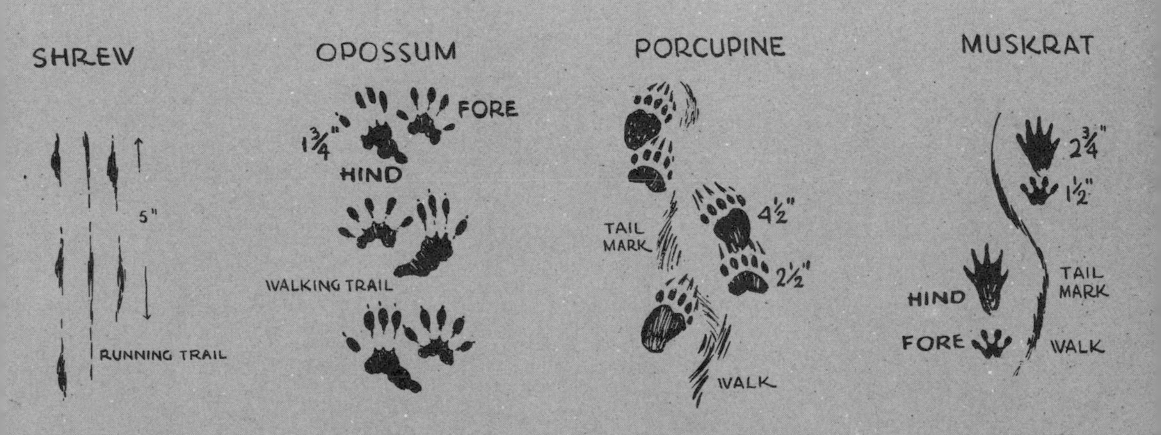
TOE AND HEEL WALKERS
SHREW
5"
RUNNING TRAIL
OPOSSUM
1¾"
FORE
HIND
WALKING TRAIL
PORCUPINE
TAIL MARK
4½"
2½"
WALK
MUSKRAT
2¾"
1½"
HIND
FORE
TAIL MARK
WALK

this fact. Other animals, when galloping, have similar track patterns, but with mice, squirrels, and rabbits, the mink and weasel too, the pattern is typical since they seldom travel any other way.

Animals that bound have two characteristic positions of the forefeet: paired, or with one a little in advance of the other. The paired position is typical of tree squirrels such as red and gray squirrels, and the other typical of the rabbit. Ernest Thompson Seton makes a generalization regarding this which he feels holds up rather well, with occasional exceptions for individual animals or unusual circumstances. He says that as a rule, tree climbers, tree squirrels and white-footed mice, for example, use the paired position of the forepaws, while the terrestrial animals, rabbits and most mice, place one forefoot ahead of the other.

Animals that Run on Their Toes

One very common track everywhere is that of the house cat. A cat, like other animals that run, is digitigrade; it walks on its toes. Its toe prints are arranged one before the other to form a single line. This is accomplished by carefully placing the hind toes in the impressions made by the front. One feature of the cat track which at once sets it apart from that of the fox or dog is the absence of claw marks. A cat walks with its claws retracted.

Fox tracks are similar to a cat's in that they too are in single file, but claw marks are present and the marks of the toe pads are smaller than a cat's. Dog tracks are less in line than the fox's and the toe pads are larger. In deep snow, however, toe pad marks and claw marks are hard to distinguish. Sharp, deep prints in mud are far more clearly defined.

A deer is another animal that walks digitigrade, but the prints of its two little hoofs easily identify it. It is often possible to identify the tracks of individual deer by paying close attention to size and slight variations in the print of a single hoof.

Animals That Walk on Heels and Toes

Digitigrade animals are usually those that rely on speed to elude enemies or to overtake their prey. The more deliberate animals walk plantigrade, touching heels and toes to the ground. The porcupine with its quills and vegetarian diet has little need to hurry, and similarly, the skunk with its potent weapon and omnivorous appetite has slight occasion for running. Likewise the bear, raccoon, and opossum, with varied menus and ability to climb when danger threatens do not need to rely on speed. The tiny shrew is another that plants its heels on the ground as it sets about eating its own weight in insects every day, a task requiring patient and careful searching. In fact, the short-legged shrew often seems to plant its whole body in the snow, at least in soft snow, so that it appears to travel in a sort of groove that disappears now and then in a winding tunnel through the snow. The woodchuck, ever within easy reach of its protecting burrow, walks plantigrade, bounding to its hole if danger threatens. Woodchuck tracks are seldom seen in snow for these animals hibernate in winter.

Tail Marks

Tail marks, when present, are an important part of a track pattern, either helping to distinguish it, or to serve as a clue to the activity taking place at that point. The tail makes a characteristic part of a muskrat track, forming a strong curving line between the rows of paw marks. The tail mark also helps to identify a white-footed mouse track. It forms a straight continuous line not only between the paw marks but even between the bounds unless they are exceptionally long ones. The shrew drags its tail too, but its ambling gait obviates any confusion with the trail of the white-footed mouse. Opossums drag their tails, and as they seldom hibernate, except during periods of extreme cold, their tracks are often seen in snow. When present, the big toe mark spreading wide from the rest of the hind foot, like the thumb of a human hand, identifies the trail. In deep snow, foxtails leave a brush mark at one side of the trail, and mink tails drag occasionally to form a line. The cottontail rabbit's tail makes a small round mark in the snow when the rabbit sits.

Bird Tracks

The shape and size of the print and the number of toes showing, together with the gait—whether the bird walked or hopped—help to distinguish bird tracks. Sometimes there are semicircles of separate marks made by the tips of the wing feathers where the wings brushed the snow in taking off. In winter a fringe of hairs grows out from the ruffed grouse's toes, acting as a sort of snowshoe to help support its weight on top of the snow. Often this fringe shows plainly and will identify the track.

How to Make Casts of Animal Tracks

Find a sharp, clean-cut footprint of an animal in mud, sand, or wet snow; stand a cardboard collar around it. Mix plaster of paris and water until just thin enough to pour, and fill the track to the top of the collar. Allow the plaster to harden for about fifteen minutes. You should then pick up the plaster, collar and all, and wrap it carefully

Upon landing, a ring-necked pheasant leaves a distinctive track in snow

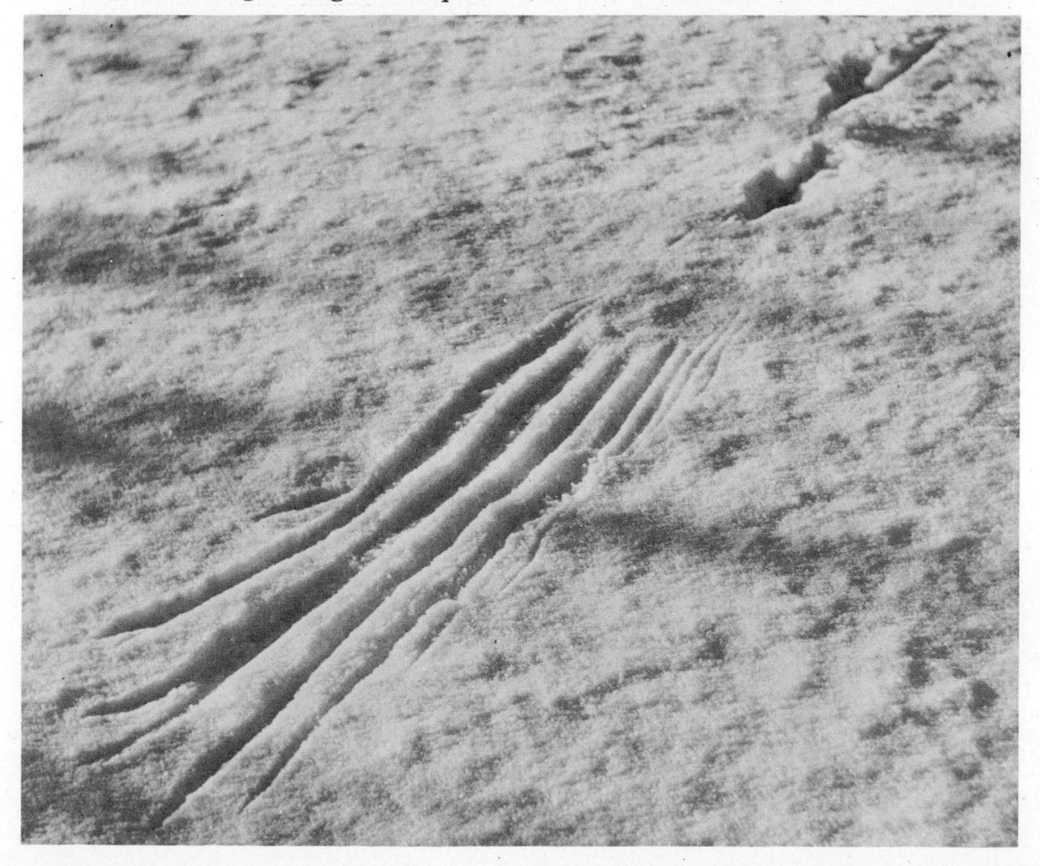

Tracks of a squirrel in snow

in paper while it is still slightly soft to prevent rubbing. When it is dry and hard, brush off any sand or mud that may be clinging to the track and you will have a negative or raised cast of the footprint. To make the positive, grease the negative cast, fit a cardboard collar around it and fill with more plaster of Paris. This second cast will be the positive, showing the sunken impression of the animal's foot just as it appeared in the mud or sand. —D.A.T.

Recommended Reading

Animal Tracks—George F. Mason. William Morrow and Company, New York.

Animal Tracks—The Standard Guide for Identification and Characteristics—Introduction by H. Marlin Perkins, Director, Lincoln Park Zoo. The Stackpole Co., Harrisburgh, Pennsylvania.

Field Book of Animals in Winter—Ann Haven Morgan. G. P. Putnam's Sons, New York.

A Field Guide to Animal Tracks—Olaus J. Murie. The Riverside Press, Cambridge, Massachusetts.

Colors of Animals

Among those who are just beginning to be aware of birds, few become interested in them through hearing their songs; in fact, the average individual is scarcely conscious of bird music until it is called to his attention. Neither is the flight of birds, marvelous as that power may be, likely to kindle enthusiasm in the casual observer. But color is the touchstone to genuine attention and interest.

A group of more or less indifferent students may go into the field during early May, to sit down quietly near a tangle of blooming dogwood and crab apple. When they see for the first time a redstart or a magnolia warbler, they find in these feathered mites color and beauty such as they had not imagined, never having really looked before at a bright-plumaged bird. To these students birds will never again be dull, uninteresting, nondescript. Such observers may never become ornithologists, but all will have lasting impressions of rich and pleasing color and the memory of a few birds, at least, that have become individuals.

Certain of the standard books about birds have chapters on coloration, some of them excellent, but this information seems to be beyond the reach of the average student who is puzzled about the albino that appears at the feeding shelf, or about the reddish-brown and gray screech owls which one finds in a single nest. (*See Albinism.*)

Color as one sees it and pigment as it exists chemically are not at all the same. This is just another expression of the old saying, true of birds as of other matters, that things are not always what they seem. When a group that has just been watching a blue jay or an indigo bunting is told they were mistaken in thinking they saw blue on the bird—that there is no blue pigment in the feathers—they become frankly skeptical.

Nature has an amazing way of taking

Mallard ducks, male (above); and female

a few elements and weaving them into intricate and seemingly endless combinations. Thus in the lower vertebrates, the fishes have three fundamental pigments, brown, red, and yellow. These are blended, combined, and recombined until we have the rainbow brilliance of the reef fish in tropical waters. Obviously there are other colors, notably iridescent blues and greens, but these are due not to pigments present but to the effects of refracted light from crystals of guanin (a protein waste product) just beneath the skin surface.

Once having fixed on a pigment pattern for vertebrate animals, nature continues it, with some relatively minor, but highly interesting side excursions, through the amphibians and the reptiles to birds and mammals, and even to man himself. Brown, red, and yellow, these three and usually no more, are the basic pigments from which the coloration pattern is woven. In birds as in fishes there are of course blues and greens, but these are, for the most part, light effects, the result of refraction from certain arrangements of crystalline rods or prisms. Green pigments and blue pigments do occur, but are exceptional.

The most common pigment is *melanin*, which produces brown or black in animals. There is some dispute as to whether it is brown or black; likewise as to whether the melanin of birds is the same as that in other vertebrates.

Without exploring these points of difference, it can be said that every student of bird life knows part of the answer—birds which appear to be, and are commonly called, black in life are found to be brown when examined closely. A crow or turkey vulture looks black, but this is brown intensified. Shading and intensity depend on the number and grouping of the melanin-pigmented cells—the more there are (near the surface at least) the darker will the animal's fur, feathers, or skin appear.

Melanin occurs in varying concentrations in the skin of human beings. Eye color is due to melanin; whether the eyes are blue, green, gray or brown depends on the number and arrangement of the pigmented cells.

The yellow pigment in all classes of vertebrates is *xanthin*. Xanthin pigment (with slight variations in chemical make-up) also occurs in plants. It is responsible for the yellow sides of a bluegill, the stripes on certain salamanders, and the overall color of a yellow warbler. It occurs (also in varying proportions) in the skin of human beings. Yellow flowers and seeds in plants are due to xanthin.

Erythrin is the pure red pigment of living things and again there are slight chemical variations as between plants and animals. It is abundant in the red blood cells of vertebrates and gives color to the red feathers of a cardinal or a scarlet tanager. This red pigment is common in plants, and sometimes shows up with results that will be recalled with pleasure by those who have some rural background. Once in a while, normally yellow field corn produces a red ear, the xanthin in such cases being replaced or masked by erythrin.

According to authorities there are two other relatively rare pigments in bird feathers. One produces the vivid green feathers on the African plantain-eaters, and is called *turacin*. It is remarkable in containing a much higher proportion of metallic copper (7%) than is known from the plumage of any other birds. Violet pigments, also, have been reported from the feathers of certain tropical bird groups, although most violet color is due to structural arrangement within the feathers rather than to pigmentation.

It is interesting to trace the appearance of the three fundamental pigments, brown, yellow, and red, through a large and widely distributed family of birds, the finches (*Fringillidae*). Apparently the brown pigment, melanin, is basic. Most of the adult sparrows, and most young birds throughout the entire family, have more or less brown in their plumages. It can be fairly assumed that the finches began their development as a group of rather plain brown birds.

But such drab raiment has not sufficed for these birds. Many of them have evolved toward brighter hues, and along remarkably parrallel lines. Some, such as the male cardinal, have achieved a startlingly bright shade of red. The male purple finches, plainly striped in brown when young, have taken on an erythric wash, as have the redpolls, the rosy finches, and the crossbills. In some the evolution (thus far at least) has been toward yellow. In this group are the American goldfinch and the evening grosbeak. Among some species the males have achieved the red coloration while the females have traces of yellow in their plumage. Pine and rose-breasted grosbeaks and red crossbills are notable for this tendency.

Jaguar cub

Various authors have used the siskins and goldfinches of America and Europe, close avian relatives, to point up this evolutionary trend toward plumages that make greater use of erythrin and xanthin. The American pine siskin is a striped brown sparrowlike bird with flashes of yellow in wings and tail. Its European counterpart is much more strikingly colored, with wings and tail about half yellow. Skipping back to this side of the Atlantic, we find the eastern goldfinch, a vivid yellow-and-black bird without streaking. Finally, the European goldfinch, seemingly farthest advanced along this line of development, is a yellow-and-brown bird with a bright red patch on the face. Perhaps these four closely related species epitomize the course of fringilline evolution.

Albinism

Anyone who thinks about the matter will recall that some birds have no pigmented feathers, but are pure white in plumage. It seems perfectly right that American and snowy egrets, and white ibises, as well as adult glaucous, Iceland, and ivory gulls, should have white feathers. The surprise comes when we see a single pure white robin among a flock of robins. An egret is naturally white but a robin is not.

The white robin, if white enough, may be, and very likely is, an albino. Strictly, an albino is a living thing, plant or animal, wholly lacking in pigment—hair, feathers, skin, eyes, in animals and leaves, stem and flowers in plants. It may seem a contradiction to say that true albinos must have pink eyes, but that is apparent rather than real, since the pink coloration is due to the presence of blood capillaries, unmasked by any pigment, near the eye surface.

The physical chemists say that the presence of pigment in any living thing is dependent on at least two factors (perhaps others as well). These two primary requirements are color bases (*chromogens*) and enzymes to act upon them. When both are present, and when they interact properly, colored products (pigments) result. If either is absent, or if the two do not interact, an albino occurs.

Albinos result from a primary mutation. Genetically, the characteristic is a recessive, which means that if an albino mates with a normal individual (so long as that normal-appearing individual is not itself carrying the concealed factors for albinism) no albinos will appear in the first generation offspring, but may in the second.

Pigmentation or the lack of it in an organism is due to the interaction of a number of different inheritance factors which are called *genes*. It may be impossible to say just how many genes will be concerned in the color inheritance of different species, but the number will certainly vary from species to species, and may be quite large. These color genes, many of them at least, may or may not act independently, so that an almost infinite variation in color detail is possible.

In the true albino all color factors have failed to act, but this is relatively rare. Much more common are the so-called "partial albinos"—something of a contradiction in terms, and rather like saying that a ball is partly round. Webster's dictionary recognizes the common usage, however, and regards as albinos those plants and animals which are abnormally white in only a part of

Albino gray squirrel

their outer covering. Partial albinos are relatively common among some species of birds—robins, house sparrows, and some of the true sparrows particularly.

Some birds will have only a few abnormally white feathers, others may have a symmetrical design in white on either side of their bodies; still others may present a mottled white and dark appearance; the variations are countless. This may be the result of the failure of one or more color-determining genes to function properly.

Egrets, white gulls, and other birds with naturally unpigmented feathers are not albinos. They have normally pigmented eyes and usually have true pigment in legs and bill. They have normal powers of vision, whereas albinos, lacking eye pigment, have weak and uncertain vision. Also they are more conspicuous than their pigmented brethren, and less able to sense the dangers which are certain to threaten them. Furthermore, when white feather coloration (a loose and inaccurate phrase, but hard to avoid) is the normal thing, it is a dominant characteristic, genetically speaking, and the birds will breed true to type, something which does not happen among albinos.

Albinism occurs among all living things. In green plants it is usually fatal, since the plant must have the green pigment, chlorophyll, for the production of its own sustenance. Ordinary field corn is subject to albinism, and W. C. Legg tells of a cardinal flower (*Lobelia cardinalis*) that was almost pure white throughout. A trillium (*Trillium grandiflorum*) was pure white throughout, save for the narrowest of green segments in one of the leaves.

Not all white plants are albinos. however. Some—the familiar Indian pipe, a saprophyte, is an example—take their food from other organic matter instead of carrying on their own manufacturing process. No chlorophyll is needed, and since there is no other prominent pigment (there is sometimes enough erythrin to produce pink Indian pipes) the plants are white without being true albinos. (*See under Saprophyte*).

Among animals the chance for survival of albinos is generally better, since the animals are not dependent on pigment for the manufacture of their own food. Both the invertebrate and the vertebrate groups produce albinos more or less regularly. Albinistic insects, crayfishes, brook trout, salamanders, snakes, and mammals of many kinds are known. Among mankind albinos occur much more frequently than many people realize. In fact, the word was coined to apply to white Negroes, these abnormalities usually being objects of superstitious veneration on the part of the African tribes. The legend of the "fair god" among the Indians of Middle America is as likely to have arisen because of the accident of an albino as from the visit of a native from the lost continent of Atlantis. One author states that an albinistic individual occurs among every 10,000 human births.

Large albinistic mammals have had a peculiar fascination for primitive people. White buffalo have been objects of worship to the plains Indians. White deer, so it is said, were regarded as spirits by the woods Indians, and were never shot. Of course the subject has also been dealt with in literature, *Moby Dick* having as its central figure a white whale. The Siamese veneration of the white elephant is common knowledge. One of the prize exhibits on the Montana National Bison Range featured an albino buffalo bull.

Albino birds of many species have been reported, and museums are likely to acquire good numbers of such specimens. Brown pigment (melanin) seems much more likely to disappear in inheritance than does red or yellow. Thus albino sparrows are fairly common, and albino crows, vultures, ravens, and blackbirds of various kinds have been reported. But albinos are much rarer among the brightly colored birds, the red and yellow pigments seldom entirely disappearing, although their intensity may be much decreased. A white goldfinch was reported with no pigmented feathers, but it was impossible to determine whether or not the eyes were pigmented.

E. A. McIlhenny, an American ornithologist, had the unusual opportunity of observing for some time the offspring of a pair of normally colored mockingbirds, both of which, however, must have been carrying the albino factor as a recessive. Over a period of years the pair produced 43 normally colored offspring and 18 albinos, a fair Mendelian ratio between dominant (normal) and recessive (albino) characters. None of the albinos survived. It was once reported that a remarkable proportion of partially white birds were in a flock of Brewer's blackbirds. Among 500 individuals 40 percent had some white in their plumage.

Reversing the procedure, color factors may occur in abnormal numbers or combinations, resulting in an intensification of pigmentation. The commonest of such processes in animals is the intensification (abnormally) of melanin, leading to darker (melanistic) individuals.

Melanism

Melanism occurs regularly among some species of birds and mammals. Black squirrels, silver foxes, and black leopards, all more or less common in some areas, are examples of mammalian melanism. A number of hawk species have melanistic phases—the well-known Harlan's hawk, for example, has been regarded until recently at least as a melanistic phase of the red-tailed hawk. It has also been possible to develop and perpetuate a race of ring-necked pheasants of much darker than normal plumage. Unlike albinos, melanistic individuals do not have the physical handicap of poor eyesight and are much more likely to survive and to breed successfully.

Among songbirds melanism is quite rare. One of the few early records notes a partially melanistic laughing gull, not a songbird.

During the summers of 1932 and 1933, a melanistic cardinal (*Richmondena cardinalis*) was reported in West Virginia. This bird, a male, was solid black on head, nape, and upper breast, save that in the crest was one unusually long pink feather. Obviously, he was a strikingly handsome individual. He was discovered after the nesting season in the first summer, but he customarily associated with a normal appearing female.

The next summer this melanistic male mated with a female that showed abnormally yellow plumage (possibly one of his own offspring). Among three young birds which left their nest, two showed yellowish-white feathers. Apparently the normal color patterns were badly upset. The male disappeared after a time. However, other melanistic cardinals have been reported, one a nearly totally black bird observed in Illinois.

A definite relationship between dark outer coverings of animals and high humidity, with resultant lessened exposure to sunlight, has been well established. Since humid conditions are likely to result in dense vegetative cover, the light exposure of forest dwellers is still further decreased. The classic ornithological example is to be found in the North American species of the song sparrow. In areas of constant exposure to light, such as the sandy Atlantic coastal plain, the high plains of the

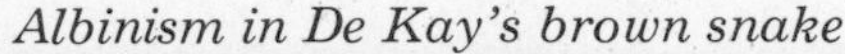
Albinism in De Kay's brown snake

West, and desert fringes, the song sparrow races are light in body color, gray rather than brown. In humid areas the reverse is true; the races are dark brown in general, becoming almost black in the dense forested areas of the northwest coastal region. In tropical rain forests the birds of the dimly lighted forest floor are likely to have somber plumage. The bright-hued species live in the sun zone of the treetops. Any amateur student who has the opportunity to study animal life in two or more diverse regions can make interesting observations of this phenomenon.

Erythrism

Erythrism, the intensification of red pigment, occurs both in birds and mammals, but is apparently rare. A classic example of natural erythrism is discussed by Dr. H. L. Stoddard in *The Bobwhite Quail*. He tells of a colony of such birds near Grand Junction, Tennessee. Over a 20-year period of observation, the birds increased in numbers and extended their range. The owner of the plantation on which the birds first appeared describes them thus: ". . . Several birds in this bevy looked to be a distinct red when in flight, and sometimes when the sun was shining they appeared to be a brilliant red . . . The auburn red is much like that of the Scotch grouse. These quail are normal in weight and habits. No birds have been introduced on to the preserve for the past 20 years. The birds in these bevies, other than the reds, are just natural, everyday bobwhite quail."

Caged birds, presumably subjected to unnatural diets, are most likely to exhibit *xanthochroism*, intensification of the yellow pigment. Parrots in captivity often increase the areas of yellow in their plumage, or may actually develop yellow areas which replace another normal color, usually green. Stoddard tells of male bobwhites that, in nature, have a yellow wash over the white of the plumage. That red and yellow

Gray and red phases of the screech owl

occasionally get mixed up in nature is attested by the recent discovery (in North Carolina and West Virginia) of a number of ruby-crowned kinglets in which the normally red feather spot on the heads is yellow or orange.

Dichromatism

Certain animals regularly have two separate and distinct color phases. This is *dichromatism*, and is little understood. To ornithologists the most familiar example is that of the common screech owl, where red-brown and gray birds often occur in a single brood. Study has shown that either sex may show either plumage phase; that two similarly colored parents may have any possible combination of the two colors in the offspring. If there is a fixed inheritance pattern it has not been discovered.

Among the examples of dichromatism in the animal kingdom is the common tiger swallowtail butterfly (*Papilio turnus*). In the northern part of this butterfly's range both sexes are yellow, with black markings. In the southern part of the range, some females are black. Occasionally there is a striking, aberrant individual with two yellow and two black wings. The timber rattlesnake also has two common color phases (although there are others not so distinct). Yellow is the most common body color, but in the heavily forested southern Appalachians some individuals, usually males, are black.

Protective Coloration

Given a few basic pigments, plus the effects of refracted light, nature has achieved blends and tints of kaleidoscopic complexity. Every serious nature student should see a copy of G. H. Thayer's fascinating book, *Concealing-Coloration in the Animal Kingdom*. Here one is introduced to the marvels of counter-shading, obliterative markings, ruptive pattern, and a hundred other matters that explain or interpret the endless variations in animal coloration. (*See also under Feather: Colors of Feathers; Protective Coloration*) —M.B.

Color Vision in Animals

Whether animals see color is an interesting question, hard to answer fully and conclusively. Humans, who see everything colored, can scarcely imagine a world totally devoid of color. For this reason the tendency at first is to assume that all other creatures see the same multicolored scenes. This is not so, of course.

Color is, in itself, such an arbitrary, intangible thing, and color sense a faculty so difficult to test or explain, that it has always been difficult for scientists to expound about it with assurance. No object really contains color, it merely absorbs the white light of daylight, as everything does, reflecting back only one of the components of that light of the spectrum. Thus a green leaf absorbs all the hues of the spectrum except green, which it reflects, thus appearing itself to be green. And again if one tries to explain to a blind person what red is without the use of comparison, it is almost impossible.

Quite apart from the widespread prevalence of partial or minor human color blindness, and the different interpretation put on the same intrinsic color by different people, it is also well to remember that man's sense of color appreciation is still being developed, and is changing all the time. For example, Homer always called the sea "wine-dark", and the ancient Greeks frequently referred to the normal human face as green.

Ultimately, everything depends on the optical receiving apparatus involved. A slight defect or variation there, and the person concerned may be partially color-blind—perhaps owing to the lack of one of the three light-sensitive "pathways" from the retina to the brain. Each transmits its own primary color—red, green, or blue. Most people who are called color-blind are in fact only partly so, having the green pathway missing, while a much smaller group lack the red pathway, and so are red-blind. These variations are physically very slight, and are confined entirely to the nervous system. There is thus the strongest evidence that animals, many of which have eyes closely similar to human eyes, lack these small features that give a color sense entirely.

From all this it will be seen just how difficult it is to apply the limited and tentative knowledge of color vision—al-

Although unable to see all colors, hawks have exceptional eyesight

ways remembering that human man may in some slight respect be color-blind—to other creatures. The subject is one that has provoked a great deal of research, much of it inconclusive.

It is endlessly difficult to be dogmatic about whether an animal can see a color. No animal can reply articulately to a direct question. Furthermore, in almost all tests made with animals it is difficult to be absolutely sure that the subject of the experiment is not choosing or distinguishing between the colors shown in terms of brightness or whiteness, and not color. For that reason, any test that is to be of value must employ colors of identical brightness and proportion of whiteness. Otherwise the creature, particularly if it is an intelligent one, may distinguish between red and green solely by brightness, just as many color-blind human beings do in tests for color blindness.

But within the obvious limitations, something is known of the subject. Enough, for instance, to say quite definitely that almost all the mammals, with the notable exceptions of the apes and the monkeys, do not see colors at all. They live in a world of blacks and whites and a fair range of grays. What they do often see quite clearly is the difference in the intensity of the blacks, and in the light intensity of the whites and grays, which not infrequently leads people into thinking that such animals as dogs, must in fact see certain colors. How many times has a fond owner of a pet dog sworn that his or her animal can always recognize a certain coat or dress when worn by someone the dog may not know, or can tell a particular dish or cushion solely by its color.

It may sound strange to live in a monochromatic world, but most mammals are nocturnal, or at least crepuscular in habit, venturing forth only when the world itself is a shadowy, dark colorless place, lit only perhaps by the pale deceiving light of the moon.

However, ordinary black-and-white movies do not seem unnatural, and most newspaper and magazine photographs are still reproduced in monochrome, yet they are recognized as a reflection of life. Even a simple black-and-white line drawing may be uncommonly natural and vivid. For all the human passion for color, its absence would be less noted than is imagined.

Dogs, cats, rabbits, rats, horses, sheep—even bulls—do not know color in the human sense of the term. A great many experiments have been made on the color vision of bulls in Spain, in connection with bullfighting technique, and though they have all shown that no bull can distinguish red as red, clear and distinct from any other shade, and that bulls generally are not in any way sensitive to red, the age-old art of the toreador and his *aficionados* with their red cloaks is unlikely to be changed. The red cloak is part of the tradition of the sport and will doubtless remain, even though those who use it know full well that it is the fluttering, taunting cloth that induces the beast to charge, not its color. A bull determined to charge will do so regardless of what color is dangled before it.

A great deal of experimenting with other mammals has achieved similar results, particularly with cats, horses, rats, and dogs. The tests usually take the form of training the animal to associate food with a particular color, while showing it at the same time another color unaccompanied by food. When the creature makes the correct choice more often than not, the color with no food attached must be gradually changed in intensity to make sure that it is not merely relative brightness that influences the subject's decision. If, at a certain stage in this color training a change in brightness is reached where the animal's reaction breaks down and it expects food equally on either color, scientists conclude it is color-blind, at least by human standards.

On the other hand, if the training holds, and the creature invariably picks the correct color to obtain food, however much the intensity of the no-food color is altered, scientists then deduce that it is able to distinguish that particular pair of colors one from another. However, this is far from conclusive evidence on color vision, so the animal must then be retrained for another quite different pair of colors. Such experiments are inevitably lengthy and difficult, and care has always to be taken that external influences such as smell, noise, position of food, time of the day, presence of other colors, and distracting lights are avoided.

Nevertheless, such tests have clearly shown the inability of most mammals to recognize colors, and the fact that the apes and the monkeys do have good color sense. In this connection between two groups of mammals, it is interesting to note that these color-conscious species are the only ones to have really bright colors on their own bodies. (It might also be claimed that they have higher intelligence, but there is no correlation between a creature's intelligence and its color sense – birds, fishes, reptiles, and insects can in many cases see colors.) One thinks immediately of the bright blues and pinks of the mandrill and other apes, whose significance in courtship rites is well known. Most other mammals have bodies of duller hue: drab grays, browns, black, fawn, in endless combinations, or white itself, which it is believed were largely evolved for unobtrusiveness or natural camouflage. Where a brightly colored animal is seen, it is usually the result of human interbreeding, as with dogs, cats, and cattle, or else is the natural camouflage shade of a creature viewed away from its habitat. The red of the dog fox, the chestnut of the squirrel, the golden-brown of the bear all merge harmoniously into their natural backgrounds. In fact, this presence of bright colors on a creature is a rough guide to color vision in nature, if allowance is made for the possibility of natural camouflage.

This is most clearly shown with the birds. They are quite different from the mammals and can see most colors with a vivid intensity. The striking plumage of almost all birds plays a big part in their courtship display, which is ready proof of their ability to see bright colors. Whether Darwin was right in supposing that the bright coloration of male birds has a survival value by being attractive to the female is a matter for conjecture. What is obvious is the part such plumage plays in a bird's life.

Birds generally see yellows, reds, greens, and oranges most clearly. They cannot distinguish blues so well – witness the comparative rarity of really bright blue birds – while as far as is known, very few birds can see violet. That shade is even less common on a bird. In addition, where blues or purples do occur in avian plumage, they are nearly always very brilliant, as with jays, kingfishers, and macaws, which seems to suggest that these shades can be

The brilliant colors of the male wild turkey help it to attract a mate

distinguished by birds only if they are unusually bright. But the Australian lyre-bird, that feathered oddity of great beauty and mystery, can distinguish both blue and violet, for it goes out of its way to select flowers of these colors with which to adorn its arbor. In the main, however, it is brilliance of color that attracts a bird, whether it be some conspicuous patch on a mate's or suitor's plumage, the petals of a flower, the shining beam of a lighthouse at night, or the glitter and sparkle of bright objects that jackdaws and magpies steal and hide away.

Experiments on birds have been rather fewer than on mammals, possibly because their ability to see colors has so obviously been demonstrated. Tests have also been almost completely confined to those species which can be kept in captivity with ease. One interesting series of experiments with the ordinary domestic hen does, however, illustrate the peculiar pitfalls present with color vision tests on birds. Grain was placed before the hens and illuminated by a spectrum of colored lights. The birds ate all the red, green, and yellow lighted grain, but left that in the blue light, from which it was not unnaturally concluded that these birds, at least, were unable to distinguish blue. Only later was it discovered, by further tests, that hens would eat blue grain with a little persuasion. The only reason they rejected it was that they never normally touch any kind of blue-colored food.

Some fishes can see certain colors. Perch, trout, shanny, minnows, and others have been proved by tests to be able to recognize a fair range of shades. Perch and other species have been regularly fed on red-stained larvae, and then easily deceived with red wool, while similar tests have been successful with food dyed yellow, orange, green, and brown. There is good evidence, too, that prawns and shrimps have a color sense. Probably all those fish species that can change their color to match their surroundings can see these, and possibly other, colors. Curiously enough, however, no conclusive tests have been made with chameleons, in spite of their well-known color-changing ability, although these creatures probably see some colors. Turtles have the faculty, and so have many lizards. Lizards known to detest salt have been trained to reject salt-soaked mealworms on paper of several different colors. On the other hand, frogs appear to be totally color-blind – or else not intelligent enough to be suitable subjects for experiment.

Insects generally have a color sense, but it varies considerably with species. There have been more tests on the color vision of bees than any other creature, which is hardly surprising in view of their value as pollinators and honey-producers. A simple experiment with bees was conducted as follows: Small squares of gray paper of different shades but equal brightness were set like the squares of a draught-board, and one blue square was included in the middle. Each square was fitted with a tiny food dish, but the blue square's dish had syrup in it. After lengthy trials a bee could be taught to fly straight to the blue square, even when its position was moved about the board. Yet when a red paper of equal brightness replaced the blue, the bee could not tell it from the grays. Bees are not only blind to reds: they live in a world of blues, purples, and yellows only, but they (and other insects) can see further into ultra-violet than man can.

Many pollinating insects are, of course, attracted to flowers as much by scent as by sight of colors—witness the popularity of willow, ivy, and lime flowers to bees. As a rule only those insects with highly developed, multi-lensed eyes have good color vision. Dragonflies probably have the best color sense in the insect world, with perhaps hoverflies, and some butterflies and moths, as runners-up. Houseflies know blue, and dislike it enough to avoid blue-washed windows, or blue walls and curtains, while mosquitoes, which are known to distinguish yellow, white, and black, appear to prefer the last-named color. In a special test made in an infested region in Oregon, seven men wore shirts of different colors. Within half a minute a black shirt had attracted the most insects—1,499 to only 520 on the next most-heavily infested shirt, a white one. —Da. G.

Animal Kingdom

Animals, like plants, are alive. Unlike plants, however, animals are capable of movement, at least at some time in their lives, and are incapable of manufacturing food from simple chemicals and the energy of the sun, as do all but a very few specialized kinds of plants. In an attempt to express the relationship between living things, scientists have devised a system of classification. The first two great divisions are called kingdoms, one for animals and the other for plants.

The animal kingdom is further divided into 28 phyla (singular, phylum), based on similarities of structure. Twelve of these phyla include the majority of all animals, all but about one percent of the total of nearly one million different kinds or species.

One phylum (Protozoa) includes all the animals of only one cell. Another (Porifera) contains the sponges, another the jellyfish and the corals (Coelenterata), and another (Mollusca), the clams, snails, and octopi.

The phylum with the greatest number of species is that of the joint-legged animals (Arthropoda); three-fourths of all presently known animal species are insects, all in one of the classes (Insecta) in the phylum.

All of the animals with backbones are in the phylum Chordata. These comprise the most familiar animals, such as dogs, horses, and birds, and also reptiles, amphibians, fishes, and a few other groups of lesser importance.

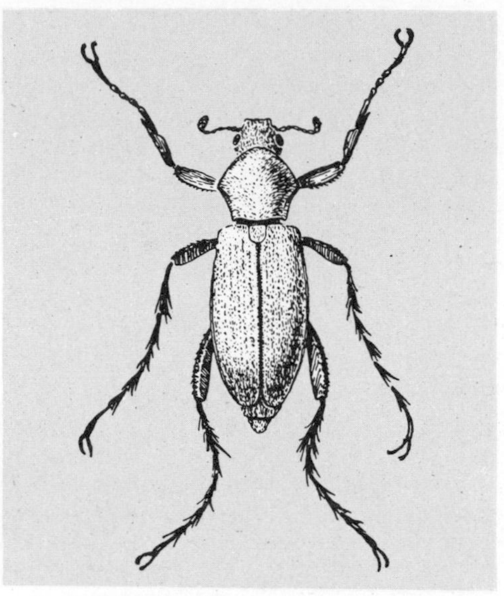

Rose chafer , an arthropod

The differences between the species are thought to have come about through the processes of evolution, and each divergence enables its possessor to better utilize some particular habitat. The animal kingdom contains such radically different species as submicroscopic ones that measure 12,700 to the inch, and the blue whale which may be 110 feet long and weigh over 150 tons. —G.B.S.

Navigation of Animals

Many animals show a strong sense of direction. Yet until about a dozen years ago, the most widely accepted explanation was one suggested by Charles Darwin and several others. According to these distinguished men, an animal retraces in reverse the route by which it is taken to a strange place.

Actually, animals take short cuts, as though they could triangulate and knew the direction to home base. Triangulation is a surveying and navigation practice in which observation of two points can establish a third.

Claims for so elaborate a direction sense did not impress scientists so long as they came chiefly from pet owners. Such stories seemed to be fanciful, overdrawn or incomplete. Except by the method Darwin suggested, how could a dog or cat find its way home over unfamiliar territory from 50 to 200 miles away? Animals have no road maps or compasses.

Of course, no one knew what route the pets took between the moment of escape at some distant point and that of arrival at a final destination. No fond owner would risk losing a pet in an experiment, or be willing to pay for a disinterested detective agency to shadow the animal for weeks if necessary, until it got home.

Animals other than pets tend to remain anonymous. Rarely can a person recognize them as individuals. Unless a chickadee has a numbered metal anklet, or a honeybee a distinctive pattern of colored paint daubed on its body, how can a person be sure when the same one is encountered a second time, or a third?

Yet millions of birds were banded and recovered before anyone found a clear answer to the question: Do migrating birds follow older, experienced members of the flock, or rely upon their own inner navigational sense?

The late Professor William Rowan of the University of Alberta (Canada) released some young crows he had raised indoors long after all other crows had left the Edmonton area and the ground was covered with winter snow. Several of the banded youngsters were recovered subsequently along the route they took—straight for Oklahoma, where Albertan crows of all ages go for the cold months. They were following a direction sense acquired in the egg. No parent birds or familiar landmarks could have helped them. They had no memory of past experiences.

Instinctive awareness of the correct direction for travel is stronger than any need to imitate. European birdbanders discovered this after they replaced the eggs of West German storks with stork eggs from East Germany.

The hatchlings received numbered bands and were watched until fall migration time. Then, when the West German foster parents set out for the Nile Valley by way of southern France, Gibraltar and the north coast of Africa, the fledglings raised from East German eggs went another way. They headed southeast and eventually joined flocks of East German storks, which migrate to the Nile Valley around the eastern end of the Mediterranean Sea

Triangulation is a surveying and navigation practice in which observation of two points can establish a third

through Greece and Asia Minor. Each East German bird separated at migration time from the common flock to travel on its own.

Similarly, no memory for turns or landmarks, and no parental guidance can explain the ability of marked monarch butterflies from eastern Canada to fly as far as San Luis Potosi, in Mexico, some 1,870 miles distant. Yet, after these insects have wintered in the warmer parts of America, enough of them return each spring to insure new broods of monarch butterflies from caterpillars on Canadian milkweed plants.

So astonishing are habits of this kind that they make one wonder about even the basic tenets of science. Are sense organs the sole channels of communication between an animal's nervous system and the outside world? Admittedly, this belief is an article of faith. Do the navigational and homing abilities of animals refute it, or is man merely insensitive to cues from the environment that are adequate stimuli for other animals?

It is not enough for one to recognize that direction sense is essential for birds, fishes, whales, bats and insects in migration, or for nonmigratory animals that return home reliably after being taken to unfamiliar territory. The extent of their ability is so great that one must find out how they know which way to turn.

Some people do have a vague sense of direction . . . but confidence is far greater when a magnetic compass is available. Only seven centuries have passed since the first loadstones, and knowledge of how to use them to magnetize a compass needle came from China to Europe.

Even the spelling of loadstone (or lodestone) no longer shows that the piece of magnetite ore was a *lead*stone —*leading* the navigator in relation to the earth's magnetic lines of force.

But do animals have compasses or some other means for getting magnetic directions? Hundreds of pigeons have been put into flight with strong magnets fastened underneath their wings in the belief that any magnetic sense they might have would be upset. The birds found their way to the home roost from many miles away in record time, despite the extra load.

Discoveries that lampreys and fishes emit pulses of direct-current electricity to which their skins are sensitive may provide an answer to the questions concerning magnetic sensitivity in aquatic creatures.

Perhaps the mud snail, *Nassarius,* relies upon something similar, for statistical studies of its creeping trails at different times of the solar day and lunar day suggested to Dr. Frank A. Brown, Jr., of Northwestern University that it orients in relation to *internal magnetic compass needles* which in turn are hands of horizontal solar- and lunar-day 'clocks.'

The nature of the internal "compass needles" remains entirely unknown. That it may prove to be a basic feature of living things is suggested by the discovery that roots of peppergrass seedlings grow to align themselves in relation to geomagnetic forces.

If an animal could know its direction of travel and estimate its elapsed time and speed, it might use the equivalent of a human navigator's method of "dead reckoning." The late Werner Ruppell found that young hooded crows in Europe fitted this pattern.

He captured 900 at Rossiten on the Baltic coast of East Prussia on spring migration, and banded them all. He released 400 immediately. The rest he took quickly to Flensburg, at the south end of the Danish peninsula, 465 miles due west. There he freed them in a region never visited by this kind of crow.

As his banded birds were recaptured, Ruppell plotted their flight on a map. Those released at Rossiten had all continued into their normal breeding areas east of the Baltic Sea. Those freed at

Flensburg were caught in northeastern Denmark and in Sweden—all but one of them within an area resembling in form and dimensions the proper breeding territory—but displaced 465 miles westward.

These had continued in their normal migration direction for approximately the correct distance, and settled down. The only individuals that did not continue to shuttle back and forth each year, parallel to their relatives, were a few mature birds that had been captured by mistake. They seemingly recognized that their route was not taking them to the proper breeding region, and gradually worked back into their customary summering and wintering areas.

Even for dead reckoning, a navigating animal or man must know direction. Dr. G. V. T. Matthews of Cambridge University insists that pigeons and other birds get their cues from the sun, and that they can compensate for the varying angle toward the sun as each day progresses—low in the east at sunrise, high to the south at noon and low in the west at sunset.

According to his observations, a few minutes are sufficient for a pigeon to detect the arc the sun follows through the sky and for the bird to predict the arc to its highest point (due south). This is expecting a great deal of the bird's eye and brain, for the earth's rotation shifts, the sun's position only about half the sun's apparent diameter each minute.

Yet, Dr. Matthews credits birds with far more than this ability to estimate the sun's arc accurately. He claims for them the equivalent of a sextant and a chronometer running on "home time." With these they can learn their geographical location anywhere on earth from the angular height of the sun at noon and the hour according to "home time" when it will reach this highest position for the day. The height will give the latitude, and the home time of noon provides the relative longitude of the place. (*See also under Homing*)

Anyone doubting that birds possess these instinctive skills is left with the difficult task of proposing an alternative, simpler explanation for the demonstrated ability of banded Manx shearwaters to fly separately over trackless seas from release points in America, for 3,050 miles in 12½ days to their own burrows on an island off the west coast of England.

This performance required an average speed of better than 10 miles per hour, day and night, or faster travel if the bird stopped at intervals to feed and rest. Each one must have sensed where home was in relation to America, even though Manx shearwaters never normally venture so far from the Isle of Man.

The sun is so conspicuous a skymark that no one doubts a bird's ability to see it. One's only hesitation is in accepting the flier's suggested talent for using the sun's position and arc in so sophisticated a way. Only a navigational instrument of considerable complexity can enable a human flier to adjust his direction automatically in relation to the sun as it follows its regular path from east to west.

To use the moon, when it is visible at night, in a corresponding fashion—as has been claimed for birds migrating after sunset — would require reference to a lunar clock with a 24.8 hour day—measured from moonrise to moonrise.

Birds do migrate by moonlight. They also travel under the stars, with no moon, but seldom start out in cloudy or foggy weather. Could it be that these fliers are instinctively alert to the major constellations and can direct their flight by celestial navigation?

Dr. E. G. F. Sauer of Freiburg, Germany, raised some night-migrating warblers in confinement, where they could get no glimpse of the heavens, to the age at which they normally would have begun their southward flights to wintering areas. He took the fledglings in a closed box to the planetarium in Bremen and uncovered their cage only after the dome above was illuminated solely by the projected replica of the major stars. The warblers promptly adjusted their position in the cage to face in the direction their parents were already flying.

When the caged birds were covered once more, the attendant rotated the imitation sky until constellations that should have been to the south appeared instead in the west. The cover was then removed. The birds adjusted their resting positions 90 degrees and again faced the southern stars—now in the west. Nor did they alter their heading when the planetarium machinery was set in motion, slowly shifting the star pattern as it would appear to do through the earth's rotation. Actual directions meant nothing to the birds; they were navigating from celestial cues.

Even an electric lamp bulb shifted smoothly through an arc the sun might follow is enough guidance for a caged bird to turn and face the direction it would fly if free.

A few years ago Professor Victor C. Twitty of Stanford University realized that he did not know whether the salamanders, whose embryos he had been studying, lived more than a year or two, nor did he know whether they regarded as home the particular stream along which they laid their eggs. He therefore began marking as many as 262 male salamanders from a single pool, releasing them there again at once. Year after year the same individuals returned to the stream and were recaptured, tallied, re-marked and released. Almost without exception they returned to the same pool.

In the seventh year after the experiment began, 32 percent still returned—faithful to the particular segment of the stream—from among a larger number known to be still surviving. Between breeding seasons, the professor was sure that all left the water. The population redistributed itself over the adjacent mountainsides, where the salamanders hide underground during the dry summer months.

Professor Twitty decided to relocate some of the distinctively marked salamanders to see if they could find their way back to the place where he had originally found them. Of nearly 1,000 females, 18 managed to get home in the third year from a distance of three miles; they had surmounted a ridge more than 1,000 feet above the stream level, to reach the pool they recognized as home. How did they find their way?

Visual clues must be ruled out. Salamanders, deprived of sight, reach their own breeding pools overland from a mile away. Touch is not necessary. In a star-shaped horizontal pen floored with plastic sheeting, they crawl slowly in the correct direction. Tilting the surface they rest on has no obvious effect. Apparently salamanders do not "feel their way home." Odor still is a possible sensory avenue for navigational guidance. Yet how could a salamander smell something distinctive about its own pool from three miles away and the other side of a ridge?

The Italian entomologist, F. Santschi, in the second decade of this century, tried to account for the ability of North African ants to return to the nest.

By erecting a high fence around an ant he prevented it from seeing any landmarks. With an opaque disc he shadowed the ant, concealing the sun's direction. And still the ant took the correct turns to hurry home. Santschi concluded that ants could see the stars and steer by them, even by day when to man's eyes the sky seemed uniformly blue. (*See also under Ant*).

Far more surprising was the explanation uncovered in 1949 by the master experimenter, Professor Karl von Frisch of Munich. He was seeking to discover how domestic honeybees communicated within the hive. How could a worker, freshly back from finding a source of

Birds navigate by the sun and the stars.

sugar water, tell a dozen other bees exactly how far to fly and in which direction?

Through a red pane of glass in the side of a hive, von Frisch watched returning bees that he had marked distinctively. They performed special little dances on the vertical honeycomb, while other workers crowded close. Whenever a bee from a feeder 10 yards from the hive was dancing, it followed a circular pattern—always reversing its direction regularly at the same place in the circle. Any bee from a feeder 1,000 yards distant performed a figure-eight dance, looping to the left around one circle, to the right around the other, with a tail-wagging run along the part of the pattern between the two circles.

In these unlike dance patterns, von Frisch recognized how a worker showed the difference between "near" and "far." The far signal—the figure-eight dance—was also faster for food discovered at 100 yards than for sugar water two miles away. At 100 yards the dancer outlined about five complete patterns in each quarter of a minute, whereas at two miles, it performed a single figure-eight in the same time.

Von Frisch noticed that for sugar far from the hive, the "tail-wagging" run in the figure-eight dance varied in direction both with the time of day and direction from the hive to the food. Bees wagging as they *ascended vertically* on the honeycomb were indicating food to the east in early morning, to the south at noon, and to the west toward sunset.

At noon, a returning worker full of sugar water from 200 yards away wagged while *descending* the comb if the feeder was north of the hive, wagged while running horizontally to the left if the feeder was east of the hive, and performed its signal while running to the right if it had found food west of the hive.

In every case, the angle between the tail-wagging run and the vertical on the honeycomb corresponded to the angle the worker bees should fly from the hive, using the sun as a skymark. The point of reversal in the "round dance" similarly gave the angle at the hive between food and sun. Herein lay the bee's means of communicating direction. Von Frisch described it as the "language" of the bees.

Like Santschi with his North African ants, von Frisch was puzzled to find that bees in Munich could still give and receive directions when the sun was hidden from sight by thick clouds, so long as a generous area of blue sky remained in view. Von Frisch had one advantage over Santschi. Polaroid sunglasses had been invented in the intervening years, and von Frisch was well aware that the seemingly uniform blue sky varies greatly in the angle of polarization (the angle at which light vibrations, reflected from a transparent surface assume a straight-line pattern perpendicular to the ray shown by the scattered light reaching the observer's eye).

Although the pattern is invisible to man without the aid of polaroid materials or a Nicol prism, the compound eyes of insects might be detecting it. Using ingeniously simple tests with polaroid sheeting, von Frisch proved that bees were indeed taking their cues from the polarized sky light as though it were a compass. With an internal "clock" compensating for the sun's apparent movement through the day, the insects used their "sky compass" for navigating successfully and for communicating direction within the darkness of the hive.

Recently, further exploration was accorded the bees' use of a sky compass and an internal "clock," by shipping colonies on fast airplanes from one part of the world to another. French bees, shipped to New York, needed experience with the sun rising on a new schedule before they were able to reset their internal "clocks" and forage properly on

The salamander finds its way home from a distance of more than a mile

New World time. New York bees in Paris require a similar period of adjustment.

But when bees are shipped from the northern hemisphere to the southern, they seem unable to learn their way about. The sun compass is reversed in the southern hemisphere, with the sun to the north at noon. Apiarists are finding that the ability of these insects to compensate for the sun's apparent movements east to west is inherited, with one mutation useful north of the equator and its converse needed in the southern hemisphere. (*See also under Bee: Life of the Honeybee*)

If the compound eye is particularly well adapted toward detection of the sky's planes of polarization, then sky compasses might be important to a really great variety of creatures. More than three-quarters of the species of the animal kingdom have compound eyes. They are the insects on land and in fresh water, the horseshoe crabs that scavenge over the sandflats and into deeper coastal regions, and crustaceans with a multitude of habits (*See under Insect; Crustacean*).

The sandhopper, *Talitrus,* along the Adriatic side of the Italian peninsula will automatically turn east and scurry toward salt water if taken inland. Near Naples or any shore facing Corsica and Sardinia, the sandhoppers go west to Tyrrhenian safety. If a Neapolitan sandhopper is transported to the Adriatic coast, it still turns west—away from the sea and toward mountains it could never cross. In foreign territory the sandhopper's inherited direction sense brings disaster. But so long as each population remains within its normal home territory, its sky compass proves valuable.

The Italians, F. Papi and L. Pardi, who discovered these differences between east-coast and west-coast sandhoppers in their country, realized that night is the usual time for such crustaceans to be active on the beach. Astonishingly, the sandhoppers proved able to orient themselves correctly in moonlight. They waited until the moon rose and then set out on their travels in search of food. But could they guide themselves if the moon was hidden from them by some opaque object? Had they any counterpart of the celestial navigation ability Santschi suggested? Had they to wait until moonrise to set their clocks each night?

No one was ever really satisfied that ants could see stars in the sky by day. It is equally implausible that sandhoppers can detect any polarization pattern in the night sky, or that they can see the constellations. Sandhoppers are about as blind as bats. Neither will respond to a pattern of imitation stars.

Yet we know that insect-eating bats from northern latitudes include several kinds that migrate for hundreds or thousands of miles, even out over open ocean where they have no landmarks that would give a meaningful echo of an ultrasonic cry. How, then does a bat find its way over the ocean by night? Perhaps it relies upon sensory cues of which we are unaware—something no one has yet suspected.

The animal sky compass, like echo location, is a recent discovery. One has every reason to expect further exciting revelations. —L.J.M. and M.M.

ANOPHELES (*See under Fly*)

ANT

One of the most successful of all the insect families is that of the ant. The various species have adapted to an exceptionally wide range of foods and of habitats. The number of individuals, even in an area of half an acre, may be astronomical, for colonies number from a few members to several hundred thousand. More ants are present in any one locality than can be seen, as a large proportion of any nest is always busy in the galleries, and there are some species in which the workers never appear above ground.

There are at least 3,500 recognized species of ants in the world, and possibly an equal number have yet to be named. All belong to the family Formicidae, one of the major groups of the order Hymenoptera, which includes bees and wasps. The structure of ants indicates that they have descended from a form of wasp; some species still have a wasplike stinging organ. Most species manufacture a poison which they squirt into wounds made by their pincers.

—G.B.S.

Some Habits of Ants

Concerning ants, there are any number of "stranger than fiction" facts. For example, these little insects are sometimes found atop the Empire State Building, more than a hundred stories above the sidewalks of New York City. How do they get there? Perhaps they are carried aloft by winds. This is a strong possibility but has not been proven. Some day careful investigation by a scientist—or by a layman who happens to be interested in the habits of ants—may provide a definite solution to the mystery.

However, one does not have to look in unusual or out-of-the-way places to become fascinated by these creatures. They are found in backyards, gardens, fields, and woodlands; they swarm from under sidewalk pavements and often invade homes in search of food. Not only may they be watched under such circumstances, but it is possible to make or buy an ant nest and keep it under observation in home or classroom.

In the past few years "ant palaces" have become a popular item sold in

The long antennae of the ant are highly specialized sensory organs

hobby and toy shops. A space between two sheets of glass on a stand allows for soil and ants to be inserted. Then, if the insects are properly provided with food and water, they may be observed at work—a miniature colony in action.

At least two other extremely satisfactory man-made ant nests have been invented for the study of ant life, and either may be made at small expense. One, known as the Janet Ant Nest, is of cast plaster, with narrow passageways connecting shallow chambers molded into the plaster and a sheet of glass covering the entire piece. Some of the chambers serve as nests. These are given an opaque cover to provide darkness. One chamber is used for food and this is not darkened. Especially recommended for use in schoolroom study is the Lubbock Ant Nest. Detailed directions for its construction may be found in the *Handbook of Nature Study* by Anna Botsford Comstock.

Industry Rewarded

Since the Biblical admonition, "Go to the ant, O sluggard. Consider her ways and be wise," ants have enjoyed a reputation for industry and (despite heated objections from some scientists) for intelligence. Certainly these insects with their highly organized social order, in which three classes of society flourish, have been infinitely successful in survival. And they seem to thrive under modern conditions every bit as well as they did before cities and farms replaced fields, woodlands, and meadows. Whether "intelligence" or "instinct" is the term which should be used to describe their behavior, ants are well worth observing.

There are many species of ants, all quite similar in body formation but varying in size and color. They may be black, brown, reddish, or yellowish. A colony is made up of three principal kinds of individuals: the queen (a fertile female), the infertile females which act as workers and soldiers, and the males. The type commonly seen at picnics, in the home, or on sidewalks is the worker. It is not much of an exaggeration to say that anyone can recognize an ant. However, there are possibilities for understandable confusion in recognition. For instance, the winged forms that are produced once a year may be mistaken for wasps, and wingless forms are frequently confused with worker termites. An ant's most obvious contrast with the termite is its restricted abdomen, giving it a definite "waist" which the termite does not have. A true ant also has one or two roundish segments in the constricted part of the abdomen which are considerably enlarged.

In any typical ant colony the outstanding figure is the queen. Exalted as this title may sound, the ant queen is not a ruler but a virtual egg-laying machine. Frequently she is the sole founder of a colony. A queen needs mate only once to be able to lay fertile eggs continuously for the rest of her life—perhaps fifteen or more years. The "marriage flight" takes place on a fine, warm summer's day, with broods of winged males and females rising skyward. Sometimes mating occurs in the air, or it may not be until the partners come back to earth. After mating, a male soon dies, but the queen bites or scrapes off her wings, digs an excavation in the soil, then produces her first brood and tends them to maturity, feeding the young from her mouth. As soon as the young are able, they begin caring for the queen mother and enlarging the nest.

Worker ants are produced from most of the eggs. The duties of these infertile females are unending. Not only do they forage for food supplies but they bring them back to the nest to feed the colony. Then come their duties toward the eggs and young, with the nest itself always waiting for attention. Whenever necessary workers fight to defend their colony, but the soldier ants frequently help with the fighting. These warriors differ from workers mainly in having larger heads and stronger jaws.

The Indispensable Antennae

Anyone who has an opportunity to observe ants either under natural conditions or in a man-made nest will be intrigued by the way they use their antennae. The most obvious use of this equipment is in feeling their way, investigating any obstacle which may lie in their paths. But further than this, they seem to "talk" to each other with them. When two ants meet they are likely to cross antennae and pat each other with the little projections. If they are sisters—that is, belonging to the same colony—they may stand together for some time with antennae fluttering. There seems little doubt that they are communicating with each other.

The ant that is cleaning her antennae (and this is something ants do with faithful regularity) unwittingly puts on an amusing show. On her front legs are hairs which form a neat little brush. She usually begins her grooming by lifting a leg over one antenna and pulling the antenna through the brush. She then cleans the brush by pulling it through her mouth. Then she cleans the second antenna in the same manner. She may follow this action with several more swipes on each side.

Possibly the most remarkable thing about an ant's antennae is that they are so much more than "feelers." Each of the five segments at the end of each antenna has its own power to detect odor. By means of the end segment the insect can distinguish her own nest from others. The next segment detects an individual scent and knows whether another ant is offspring of the same queen as her own. Through the next segment she recognizes her own scent and can thus always retrace her steps to return home. The two following segments convey information concerned with caring for the young. If she loses these end

A winged black ant queen

joints she loses all powers as a participating member of an ant colony. A detailed account of experiments which revealed these abilities was written by Adele Fielde and published in the *Proceedings of the Academy of Natural Sciences of Philadelphia in* 1901.

Besides their antennae which serve so well for "seeing" as well as "smelling," most species of ants do have eyes. They are small, however, and dull rather than shining like the eyes of a fly. (*See under Fly*)

It is the jaws that are likely to attract the attention of anyone who examines an ant closely. They are very large in proportion to the head and work sideways like a pair of shears. With them the ant seizes food and bears it to the nest. She uses them also to crush and break up hard food, to carry soil out of a tunnel she is enlarging and to lift and carry the young for which she is caring. By no means the least of the jaws' uses is to fight savagely against enemies.

Domestic Life

In a fully stocked nest—that is, one

boasting a fertile queen and workers—an observer may watch the fascinating manner in which ants take care of their young. As the queen lays her eggs, workers take immediate charge of them, massing a number of the pinpoint-sized eggs together so that they form a compact bundle. After these have hatched the larvae continue to hang together. Though the eggs do not all hatch at the same time, the worker ants feed the smaller larvae more than those that are further developed. As a result all members of a brood gradually reach the same stage of development.

Ant larvae are curious little white creatures, legless and with a curved body which tapers gradually toward a tiny head. The larvae are entirely helpless for a time and are given food that is already partly digested. Then, as they grow older, they are able to take unaided the various kinds of food found for them by their nurses. From the larval stage the pupa develops looking like a very small but plump sack tied at one end with a black string. These larvae, each about the size of a small wheat grain, are often mistakenly called "ant eggs." (The commercial "ant eggs" are ant pupae, which are sold in pet shops as food for pet turtles and other animals.) Actually the pupa is almost as large as the adult ant. Sometimes the pupae are naked, sometimes enclosed in a thin, papery cocoon.

Ant nurses not only are conscientious about feeding the oncoming generation in the colony, but they also take care that the proper temperature is maintained in the nest. During the heat of the day they move the young to chambers deeper in the ground. When the coolness of evening descends, they carry them up nearer to warm stones or pavements. The "babies" are carried with gentleness in the fierce jaws of the nurses, the pupae being held by their loose skin. Another chore carefully performed is the cleaning of larvae and pupae. The nurse ants accomplish this by licking them. When a nest is attacked, the nurses hasten to carry their charges to safety, looking first to the oldest—often those in the pupae stage.

When the young first emerge from the pupa, they often try to clean their own antennae and groom themselves generally. However they are not very adept and the nurses are still concerned with their welfare. Sometimes they help the new little ones to straighten out their cramped legs and their antennae. Often the nurses move them into more desirable positions in the nest either by locking jaws and dragging them in that fashion or by taking hold by the neck or leg. Newly hatched adults are known as "callows." They are pale in color, with eyes very dark in contrast to the body.

The Raiders

Because it is so dramatic, the slave-raiding practice of ants is often men-

A carpenter ant queen (center) is carefully tended by members of her colony

tioned. Actually this is not a custom of many species. In our own country the "sanguinary" or red ant is the slave-maker. These little creatures (no more than three-eighths of an inch in length) sometimes attack the stronghold of ants much larger than themselves. More often, however, they victimize the shy little negro ant which is abundant throughout both North America and Europe. When a slave raid is carried out, the raiders are not interested in capturing adults. Though they must fight the adults, it is the larvae and pupae they seize. When successful, the red ants carry the prizes to their own nest and there tend them carefully. As they develop into adulthood the captives make no attempt to escape from the alien territory to which they have been carried but work as diligently for their captors as they would have for their own queen.

The sanguinary ants often make their homes in old stumps or logs. When they choose to live in the soil, they nest entirely below the surface; no mounds are constructed.

Although the sanguinary ant is often called "red ant," it is a different species from the common red ant which also goes by the name of "hill" or "horse" ant. The common red ant, found far and wide in North America and Europe, does construct mounds—quite sizable ones, in fact. These ants thrive particularly in open woodlands. It is the pupae gathered from their nests that are commonly sold as "ant egg" food for various pets.

Another mound-builder is the Allegheny mound-building ant. Its structures may be four or five feet in diameter and two feet high, and a single colony may occupy several mounds. While the species ranges from southern New England to New Jersey and westward to Ohio, it is most abundant in Pennsylvania's Allegheny Mountains from which it takes its popular name.

Quite similar to the common red ant is the meadow ant. It also builds mounds (which are never more than a foot high nor more than two to three feet in circumference) but it more often locates in open spaces than in woodlands, and the hillocks it makes are usually composed of coarser materials. Meadow ants are darker in color than the red ants.

The small dark brown insects known as cornfield ants are looked upon by farmers as real pests. The reason is their curious habit of cultivating colonies of aphids. In the fall the ants set great numbers of these tiny plant-feeding insects along the roots of grasses. Then, in the spring as soon as corn is planted, their captors transfer the aphids to the corn, tending them through the summer and from them collecting secretions of sweet honeydew.

Carpenters and Honey-makers

Our largest native ant, one which is quite common throughout the eastern half of the United States, is the black carpenter. When the members of this species tunnel their homes in dead trees and logs, they are harmless enough, but unfortunately they often choose the timbers of a house or a beautiful living tree for a home site. As they chew out the wood fiber the ants prove really destructive—almost as much so as termites. The workers of the species are little less than half an inch long; a queen is nearly a full inch in length. In Europe there is a similar species called the Herculean ant.

A closely related species, the black honey ant, has an especially intriguing way of insuring nourishment during lean seasons. Certain members of a colony consume sugary excretions from plants and from such insects as aphids. This is transformed into honey and stored in the abdomens of ants which are known as "repletes." When a time comes during which ordinary food is scarce, all the other ants of the colony are free to help themselves to the repletes' honey. In Central and South America as well as in areas of our own Southwest, there is a type of ant that carries the honey-storing a step further. Here the repletes, once gorged with honey, do nothing but hang from the ceilings of their underground chambers like living storage vats. While many do succeed in serving their fellow ants, the repletes are often victimized by Indians and other native people who search for the nests and eat the honeyfilled ants with great enjoyment. Two to three hundred repletes stock an average nest.

All such facts about the quiet and industrious lives that many ants lead do not seem consistent with those sometimes encountered in adventure stories. For example, one may read of fierce ant armies marching through the jungles of South America or Africa which seem to be looking for a human victim to attack. Any such story would be a gross exaggeration, although if the ants came upon an injured person who was unable to move away, there is little doubt that they would make him their prey. Their normal victims are insects such as cockroaches and other insects that are considered pests in the tropics.

Cut in half, a decayed log reveals a flourishing ant colony at work, tending eggs

Ants on the March

The driver ants are unique in that they build no nests. They are true nomads, marching through the jungles in massed columns, while individuals forage to the right and left. When the march comes to a halt, the ants cluster around in what is called a *bivouac*. For the purpose of breeding they may temporarily settle in hollow tree trunks, or under fallen trees, or they may drive a colony of home-loving ants out of their rightful nest and use it for their own purposes. The driver ants of Africa are more formidable than those of South America. It is not unusual for them to attack and destroy snakes,

Parasol ants cut pieces of leaf, carry them back to the nest where they chew them to small pieces and pile them into storage chambers.

birds, and even mammals that happen to be in their path.

In Australia lives the bulldog ant which is claimed to be the fiercest of all. However, it does not hunt in packs and therefore seems less dreadful than the drivers and foragers. Some workers among the Australian ants are more than an inch long and they are armed with poisonous stings. Some have tremendous jumping power and can cover a foot or more in one leap.

Fascinating inhabitants of the tropics are the leaf-cutting or parasol ants which live throughout most of South America and even as far north as Texas. The size of the nests they construct is remarkable in itself. One scientist, after a trip along the Amazon River, described a nest that was from eight to nine feet deep and thirty feet in diameter. The soil excavated for such a nest forms an enormous mound—perhaps several feet high.

Parasol ants have a special need for leaves. They bring pieces of leaves into the nest, chew them into tiny fragments and pile them into the larger chambers. Here the scraps of leaf become covered with a white mold which is the food of the working insects and their brood. These expert underground farmers collect their pieces of leaves by no hit or miss method. They swarm in businesslike fashion out of the nest and follow a trail for three or four hundred feet to a species of tree that bears a proper kind of leaf. Each worker then chooses its own leaf, climbs on it and, with scissor like jaws, makes a nearly semicircular cut. The cut edge is then taken into the jaw and a sharp jerk of the head detaches the cut piece from the rest of the leaf. Now each piece is held aloft by the jaws of an ant as the little marchers start back to the nest—the pieces of leaf suggesting tiny green parasols. Sometimes so great a number of parasol ants go to work at one time that large trees are stripped of their foliage in a single night.

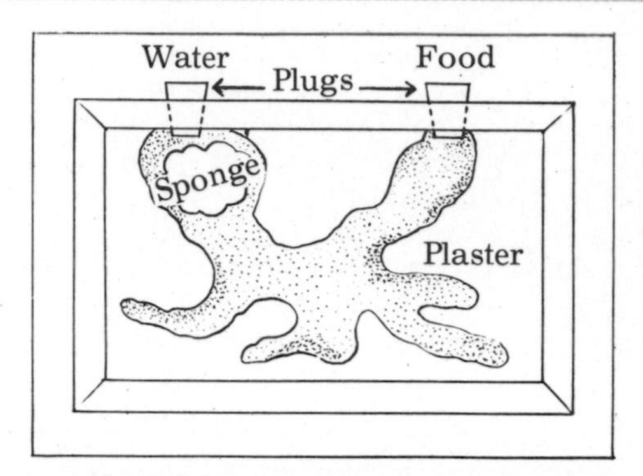

Diagram of one of the simple ant homes that may be made for indoor observations. Plaster is cast in a mold that furnishes shallow passageways between living areas. A glass cover prevents the insect inhabitants from escaping. All areas but the food chamber are covered except when the nest is being studied

Because of the remarkable nature of ant colonies, it is really not surprising that other creatures find ways to take advantage of them. It is estimated that in the world at large are several thousand different species of insects that

A carpenter ant struggles to drag home the body of a large robber fly

have become adapted to life among the ants. These include certain types of crickets, roaches and beetles. Some of these uninvited guests outwardly appear very much like the ants with which they live. Besides insects there are many instances of spiders, mites, and crustaceans making use of ant nests.

Certain of the creatures that intrude upon ants are made very welcome—for example, the tiny wingless beetles which closely resemble the small black and yellow ants among which they live. On each beetle's back are minute glands that excrete a sweetish fluid relished by the ants. As a result, the ants tend the beetles solicitously, feeding and cleaning them as carefully as they do their own offspring. The beetles, with seeming lack of gratitude, lay their eggs among the ants' brood and soon beetle grubs are consuming the young ants. However, the extent of the damage is usually not great enough to ruin the colony. More damaging are the beetles that invade the nests of the slave-making ants. These greedy intruders consume eggs, larvae, and pupae of their hosts to such an extent that a community frequently is wiped out. The beetles thereupon seek another similar nest to victimize.

Besides these enemies within the colony, there are many other creatures which prey upon ants. Bears, anteaters, birds of many kinds (especially the flicker), lizards, amphibians, and other insects (especially the ant-lion), all consume ants in great quantities. (*See ant-lion.*) Not the least of the dangers that face many ants are other ants. One colony usually shows strong hostility to another, even though it is made up of the same species, and they fight savagely over food and territorial rights. Some sting their adversaries to death. Others bite with their jaws, then spray a poisonous venom into the wounds of the victims.

Despite the enemies and hazards with which ants must cope, they continue to survive, thrive, and multiply. At the approach of cold weather, great hordes burrow deep into the ground—perhaps three feet or more—and there rest quietly. With the first signs of spring, they return to their varied ingenious and, to the human observer, thoroughly fascinating ways. —D.E.S.

How the Ant Got its Name

Long before records were kept, inhabitants of Britain were familiar with a queer little creature. It usually lived in holes which it dug in the ground, and showed great skill in cutting such hard objects as grass seeds. From that ability, it was called *aemete,* or "the cutter."

During the 12th and 13th centuries, Britons developed two distinct streams of speech. Many words with the initial syllable "ae" had the "a" stressed in pronunciation by some groups, the "e" emphasized by others. As a result, those who used the name of the ant were divided into two camps. Versions of the English Bible reflect the situation clearly, for the tiny artisan is written about in Proverbs 6:6.

John Wycliffe's translation of the year 1382 urged, "Go to the amte, thou sluggard. . . ." Half a century later, Miles Coverdale's version read, "Goe to the emmet. . . ." Publishers of the Douay version, 1609, enjoined sluggards to "Goe to the emmote. . . ."

King James gave royal sanction to the English Bible which appeared in 1611. Scholars who prepared it leaned toward the streams of speech which had influenced Wycliffe. So the famous Authorized Version read, "Go to the ant, thou sluggard." It was this version of Scripture that became the chief literary influence of the English-speaking world. —W.B.G.

Recommended Reading

The Ants—Wilhelm Goetsch. University of Michigan Press, Ann Arbor, Michigan.
Ants—Ruth Bartlett. William Morrow, New York.

ANTEATER
Giant Anteater
Other Common Names—Bushy-tailed anteater
Scientific Name—*Myrmecophaga tridactyla*
Family—Myrmecophagidae (anteaters)
Order—Edentata
Size—Body length, 75 inches; tail, 26 inches
Range—Guatemala through South America

The toothless giant anteater, which makes its home in tropical forests, is as big as a large dog, and has a coat of thick, stiff hair. It moves slowly over the ground, walking on the knuckles of the four-toed front feet. The middle claw on each fore foot is larger than the others, and is a formidable weapon when the animal is attacked. The claw is normally used in slashing open the hard, crusty covering of termite nests, or in digging in rotting wood for ants.

Anteaters have no teeth. Their tube-like snouts house a long, thin tongue which is coated with a sticky saliva. When the tongue penetrates the galleries of insect nests, the inhabitants become stuck to it, and are drawn into the tiny mouth. Anteaters also eat fruit, but only when it is soft enough to be taken in by the tongue.

The bushy tail forms a blanket for the sleeping giant anteater, which rolls itself into a ball for the night before covering itself with its bushy appendage.

Two other anteaters range north into southern Mexico. Both of these are small, and dwell in trees. The tamandua is tan with a black saddle, and has a prehensile tail. The smaller two-toed anteater is brown, and has only two toes on each front foot. The anteaters are in the order Edentata as are the sloths and the armadillos. —G.B.S.

ANTELOPE *(See under Pronghorn)*

The giant anteater has a long, threadlike tongue specialized for eating ants

ANTING

Anting is a term used by ornithologists to describe the frequent habit by birds of placing ants in their plumage.

Birds preen and clean their feathers with their beaks and claws and, in some species, with the aid of special oil glands; others, such as herons, use powder down, or simply dust-bathing. But the widespread habit by birds of placing live ants and other astringent objects and substances in their feathers is, oddly, a comparatively recent discovery in bird study.

Just why some birds should habitually anoint the least accessible parts of their bodies (usually the underparts) with wriggling ants, or a wide range of substitute irritants such as walnut juice or cigarette ashes, and why the strange ecstatic antics that invariably accompany the action should have gone unrecorded and uninvestigated so long, are but two of the many puzzling aspects of this remarkable subject.

The earliest known reference to the habit was made by John James Audubon. Writing of his 1821 observations of young wild turkeys in *The Birds of America*, he described how they "roll themselves in deserted ants' nests to clear their wing feathers of the loose scales and prevent ticks and other vermin from attacking them, these insects being unable to bear the odor of the earth in which ants have been."

This was a perceptive if indirect reference to what is now known to be a not uncommon habit. But Audubon's clue was not followed up for about 70 years, and not seriously studied until 90 years later.

The modern history of bird anting begins in 1934 with the discoveries of a man who may have done more than anyone else to bring the existing fact of bird anting before the eyes of the world—Australian ornithologist, A. H. Chisholm. The knowledge that at least 160 wild or captive species of birds use 24 different ant species and over 40 substitute materials; the many hundreds of still and motion pictures taken of it; and special experiments conducted, owe their accumulation to his vision and persistence.

Chisholm discovered the existence of anting quite by chance, and through the observation of an amateur observer. This birdwatcher was a young Australian schoolboy, Peter Bradley, living in the Melbourne, Australia, suburb of Brighton. In 1934, when Chisholm was conducting the nature notes in the *Melbourne Argus*, young Bradley wrote to him that he had seen starlings place live ants beneath their wings. *Why did they do so?*

Chisholm confesses that this letter made no particular impression upon him until he reread an almost identical query from a Sydney man dated 1927, also concerning starlings.

Chisholm included a reference to this unusual habit in a book he was writing at the time, *Bird Wonders of Australia*, published in 1934. This was read outside Australia. In June 1935, Chisholm heard from Dr. Erwin Stresemann, of the University of Berlin, of an account, published in a German scientific journal in 1929, of crows sprawling with obvious delight in mounds of red ants. Stresemann reopened the subject in this journal by quoting what Chisholm had written and asking readers to let him know if they had seen a similar practice.

By September 1935, what Chisholm calls "an impressive body of information" was made available from many German correspondents who had seen ants used by birds, particularly by aviary-bred starlings and other species. These correspondents likened the practice to dust-bathing and compared the palpable pleasure it gave the birds with that bestowed when a bird's neckfeathers are ruffled by a human hand. Some quoted long-forgotten German records of identical behavior, dated 1909, 1911, and 1912, and told of birds being seen rubbing themselves also with such

Bird anting

things as mealworms, orange juice, beer, vinegar, and cigar butts.

Stresemann called the practice "a widespread impulsive action" and "a means to destroy or expel plumage parasites," and coined the German word *einemsen* to describe it. This was later translated into English as *anting*, and is now invariably used to mean the application both of ants and other stimulants by birds to their plumage.

In 1945, T. V. Givens carried the mystery into still deeper waters with an account of red-browed finches anting in the smoke of an Australian bush fire, a circumstance one would have thought likely to inspire only fear in wild creatures.

The importance of heat was further disclosed by Maurice Burton of the London Natural History Museum, first in press articles in the *Illustrated London News* (1955) and subsequently in his remarkably interesting book *Phoenix Re-born* (1959).

Working with tame European jays and especially with his pet rook, Niger, Burton was able to explore fully the close relationship between anting and the stimulus offered birds by heat – through smoke, fumes, and actual flames. Niger not only rubbed a lighted match he was offered inside his wing feathers, but when straw was set alight near him he "literally leaped on the flames, and almost literally wallowed in them." Niger's ritual fire-dancing had tremendous stimulatory enjoyment for him. Burton felt that there can be no doubt that "the fascination exerted by the flames and that exerted by ants are related; the posture assumed by the bird, and the way it behaves, are identical in both instances." He conjectured that perhaps this behavior of certain birds, in the presence of smoke or flames, is an explanation of the always puzzling phoenix legend.

A. H. Chisholm's exhaustive and up-to-date paper, "The History of Anting," in the May 1959 issue of the Australian bird journal, *The Emu*, sums up as follows:

> "In my view the general purpose of anting, in its various phases, is the stimulating and soothing of the body, and I suggest that the general effect is similar to that gained by humanity from the use of external stimulants, soothing ointments, counterirritants (including formic acid), and perhaps also smoking. Further, I suggest that anting has affinity with the impulse of birds to submit themselves to the influences of dust, water, sun, smoke, steam, and air—an impulse which even extends at times into the use of fire."

—D.G.

Adult ant-lion

ANT-LION

Small, conical pits about an inch deep in the soft, dry ground often indicate the presence of the larval form of the ant-lion, or doodlebug. The egg, deposited in the ground by the winged parent, hatches into a squat-bodied, flat-headed, burrowing larva that builds a trap for unwary ants. By flicking its head, it throws sand out of its pit. When an ant falls into the pit and then tries to crawl out, the ant-lion bombards it with debris. Once the prey has dropped to the bottom, the long jaws of the ant-lion seize it, and a poisonous fluid soon ends the ant's struggles. The fluid is also a digestive juice, turning the ant's internal organs into liquid which is sucked through the jaws. The empty shell of the ant is then flicked out of the pit, which is readied for the next comer.

After a short pupation, the adult emerges as a thin-bodied, winged insect, similar to a damsel-fly, but smaller, and with short, clubbed antennae.

All species of ant-lion belong to the family Myrmeleontidae, in the order Neuroptera, which includes lace-wings, snakeflies, and dobsonflies. Some form of ant-lion can be found in almost any dry, sandy area throughout the United States and Mexico. The adult is slightly over an inch in length, and the larva is about two-thirds of an inch from the tip of the pincers to the end of the tail.

—G.B.S.

Ant-lion larva

Ants often tend aphids because of the sweet liquid, or honeydew they exude

APHID

Aphids are small, soft-bodied insects, under a quarter of an inch long. Their importance to mankind is far out of proportion to their size. They are plant feeders, boring and sucking into stem and leaf with a set of probes housed in the tubular mouthparts, and often occurring in such numbers that they kill the plant upon which they feed. They are also important carriers of virus and bacterial plant diseases.

Aphids have an unusual cycle of reproduction that enables them to multiply to staggering numbers in a comparatively short time. In the spring the eggs that were laid the previous autumn hatch out into females. These begin producing live young as soon as they reach maturity, usually in less than a week. This generation, too, is all female, as are all subsequent ones until the approach of autumn, when winged forms appear. The flying aphids are both males and egg-laying females, which mate and lay eggs before the cold of winter kills all the adults.

Projections upon the backs of aphids exude a sweetish liquid called honeydew. This substance is relished by ants, some species of which tend the aphids as humans tend herds of cows, and cause the aphids to produce the liquid by stroking them with the antennae. Some ants manufacture a waxy fiber that may cover the body of the insect.

Most species of aphid attack only one plant, or one plant family. These pests are often named for the plant they feed upon, as spruce aphid, bean aphid, apple aphid, grapevine aphid, and others. Aphids are classified in the family Aphididae and the order Homoptera, and are closely related to scale insects, mealy bugs, and whiteflies. —G.B.S.

APLODONTIA (*See under Mountain Beaver*)

Tiger barbs are interesting fishes for a tropical aquarium

AQUARIUM

The Freshwater Aquarium

Setting up an Aquarium

The aquarium provides a good way to study not only fishes but also many other living creatures of ponds and streams. When properly started, aquariums require very little attention and give living demonstrations of the interrelations of plants and animals.

It is impossible to state hard and fast rules about the establishment and care of aquaria, but certain general instructions can be given. A tank with metal frame and slate bottom, or a straight-sided all-glass tank is best. The tank should be as wide as it is high to provide adequate air space above the water. Globes are unsatisfactory because they expose comparatively small surfaces of water to the air and the plants and animals appear distorted when seen through the curved glass. The aquarium tank should be thoroughly cleaned and about an inch of well-washed, medium-coarse sand put in the bottom, the water plants inserted and the sand packed firmly around them.

Plants are necessary in the aquarium because their green leaves produce oxygen needed by the gill-breathing aquarium animals. To avoid disturbing the sand and plants when adding the water, a small dish or flat rock should be placed on the sand and the water poured onto this. The tank should be filled about three-quarters full of water and floating plants added—it is a good idea to allow the aquarium to stand about a week to allow plants to become rooted before introducing animal life. The tank should be placed where it receives good strong light, but little or no direct sun. Too much sun overheats the water and stimulates an overgrowth of algae (small green plants adhering to the glass and to larger plants).

In a properly set up aquarium there must be a balance between the number of plants (which supply the oxygen needed by the animals), the number of animals (which supply the carbon dioxide required by the plants), and the amount of water which provides living space and carries the carbon dioxide and oxygen liberated by the plants and animals. Aquarists tell us that "one inch of fish to a gallon of water" is a good rule for goldfishes. Smaller fishes may be kept in a tank with two inches of fish per gallon. The tail must not be included in measuring the fish. When the fishes come to the surface and gasp, the tank is probably overcrowded. If scrum and bubbles form on the top, there may be decaying material in the water. The number of snails and tadpoles should also be reckoned according to size. For a 15-gallon tank, about two dozen of the tall *Vallisneria* and *Sagitaria* should be planted one inch apart along the back or window side of the aquarium. Place a dozen or so of the shorter *Cabomba* or *Elodea* in front of them. Plants will often grow better if rooted in a layer of soil (free of manure) placed beneath the inch of sand.

When water plants in an aquarium give off enough oxygen to meet the respiratory needs of the aquatic animals, and the plants in turn consume the carbon dioxide given off by the animals, the aquarium is "balanced." Snails and tadpoles act as scavengers in cleaning up excess food and dirt and in keeping down the growth of algae. Such an aquarium should continue for weeks or even months with no required changes except added water from time to time. A glass cover should be placed over the aquarium to keep out dust and dirt.

Lymnaea palustris *Planorbis trivolvis* *Physa gyrina*

Some common pond snails

The cover should be supported on thin pieces of cork to permit the circulation of fresh air in the space above the water.

Food and Feeding

One light meal daily is sufficient for fishes if there are plenty of plants among which they can browse. It should be mentioned that overfeeding is more dangerous than underfeeding. If a food ring is used to prevent spread of food among the surface plants, and the space under the ring cleared of water plants, the fish know where to seek food and can see the bits that fall to the bottom. Uneaten food should never be left in the aquarium. It should be removed with a dip tube. Prepared fish food, dried or canned shrimp, fresh clams or oysters, beef liver, live food such as Tubifex, Daphnia, and white worms (*Eychytrae*) are all useful in varying the fishes' diet.

Water Plants

Green water plants give off oxygen in bright light. Oxygen is produced as a by-product of the food manufacturing process in the green cells of the plants.

Red swordtails are popular fishes and are hardy in a balanced aquarium

It is incorrect to say that plants "breathe out oxygen." Plants respire in the same manner as animals. Some water plants produce more oxygen than others. Good varieties for the average aquarium are *Lemma* and *Salvinia*—floating plants.

Goldfishes

The goldfish, *Carassius auratus auratus,* belongs to the family Cyprinidae —carp and carplike fishes—and is a native of China. All varieties of these exquisitely colored ornamental fish have been developed from the wild goldfish of China, a very plain, olive-colored inconspicuous little fish with small fins. The Chinese, by careful breeding and cultivation, developed the first colorful varieties. Later the Japanese became interested and developed many more kinds. Now the cultivation and breeding of goldfish has spread around the world. Today, the goldfish is one of the most extensively cultivated and widely known of any ornamental fish.

Small Native and Exotic Fishes

Like goldfishes, some other of the native tiny, gayly colored fishes require a balanced tank with plenty of green plants. They are at home on ponds, streams, lakes, rivers, and estuaries from the Carolinas south to southern Argentina in the western hemisphere, and on the other side of the world are found in Egypt, Africa, Asia, and Australia.

While most of these fishes live in fresh water, some occur in brackish or even wholly salt water. There are hundreds of species used for aquaria, some natural, others cultivated. One of the most common and hardiest is the guppy, *Lebistes reticulatus*. The male of this species is smaller than the female and more highly colored. The female produces her young alive and both parents will prey on the young unless the babies can hide among green plants or are separated from their parents until too large to be eaten. Other popular exotic fishes are the swordtail, *Xiphophorus helleri;* zebra danio, *Brachydanio rerio;* angelfish, *Pterophyllum scalare;* Siamese fighting fish, *Beta splendens;* and the sail-fin molly, *Mollienisia latipinna*.

Native Fishes of Ponds and Lakes

Some of our native pond fishes are

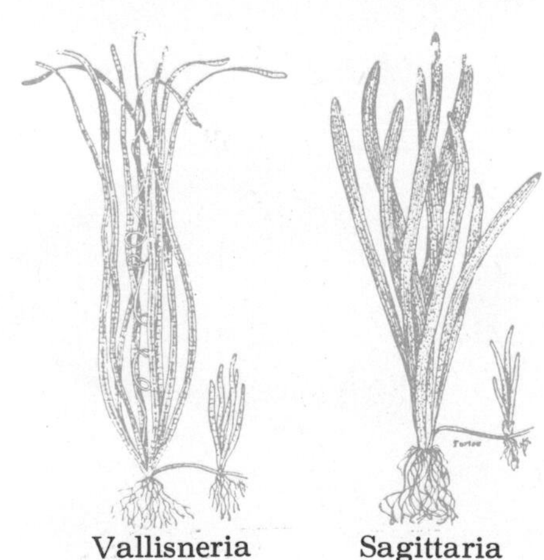

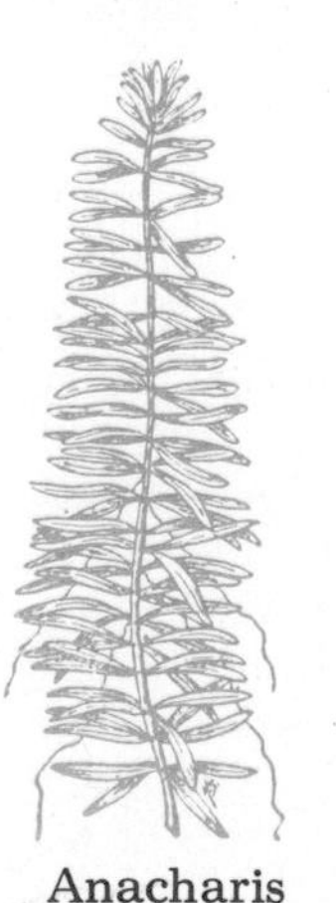

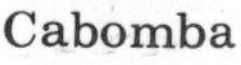

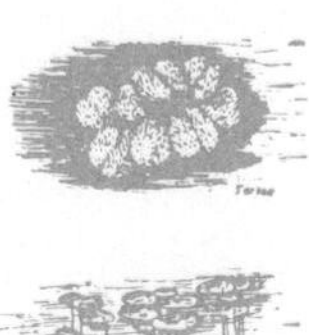

Vallisneria Sagittaria Anacharis Cabomba Lemna

suitable for the home aquarium and they often prove the most interesting. Native fishes taken from cool *running* water are often difficult to keep, but small species from ponds and lakes live well in the balanced aquarium. A permit can be obtained from the State Game or Conservation Commission for netting or seining living specimens for educational purposes. Minnows, dace, sunfishes, sticklebacks, catfishes, killies, eels, roaches, chubs, crappies, and suckers will all thrive in aquaria. The black-banded sunfish is a beautiful and very satisfactory aquarium fish. However, the sunfishes, minnows, and sticklebacks do not mix well with other species and will chase, bite, and eventually kill any other kind of fish placed in the tank with them.

Aquatic Insects and Other Invertebrates

Aquatic insects will live in an aquarium tank, a wide-mouthed glass dish, a battery jar, or other container. Because many water insects are carnivorous, they should not be kept with other water animals. Insect species living in swift running streams require plenty of oxygen and are difficult to keep alive in tanks even for a short time, unless the water is aerated frequently with an air pump. But those collected from quiet pools and ponds, especially adult beetles, caddice-fly larvae, dragonfly larvae, water-boatmen, and backswimmers do very well in aquaria. On a single collecting trip to the shore of a pond, even an amateur collector, equipped with a soup strainer, can find many common forms. Most water insects are predacious, feeding on each other and on other small animals. Their different methods of swimming, capturing their prey, feeding, and carrying bubbles of air for breathing, make them fascinating to watch. A screen over the top of the aquarium will prevent the escape of adult insects which have transformed from the larval stage. The adults can then be transferred to an insect cage.

Crayfishes, found hiding under stones or in burrows in the sides of quiet streams, will live the year around in a shallow aquarium with a layer of sand and mud, a few stones and a good supply of water plants. They will eat bits of raw meat, earthworms, and water insects. Crayfishes are crustaceans and are closely related to the edible crabs and lobsters of the sea. (*See Crayfish; Crustaceans; Seashore*)

Snails and mussels belong to a very large group of the animal kingdom known as mollusks (*See Mollusk*). There are many fresh-water species. Any pond snail or small mussel can be kept in aquaria. Snails will live in the balanced aquarium, feeding on the water plants, and will lay their eggs on the glass sides where their development can be observed within the transparent jelly masses. Pond snails multiply so rapidly that it is frequently necessary to remove many of the egg masses to maintain a balanced aquarium. To protect growing plants, the snails should be fed lettuce.

A magnifying glass, or hand lens is useful for observing the snails and other small animals.

Amphibians and Reptiles

The tadpoles of many of our native amphibians can be kept with fishes in a balanced aquarium.

A sunfish will thrive in an aquarium

Tadpoles of frogs and toads do well as scavengers. The egg masses of wood frogs, green frogs, spotted salamanders, and toads will hatch in the aquarium, thus enabling one to observe the whole interesting process of metamorphosis from egg to adult. Young tadpoles should be fed small bits of beef liver or yolk of hard boiled egg. Green frog and bull frog tadpoles require two years for their transformation into frogs and so can remain in the aquarium throughout the school year. After the terrestrial air-breathing stage of development has been reached, the young frogs or toads should be removed to a shallow water tank or to a terrarium. The tadpole breathes as a fish does, by means of gills. At first these gills are external; later internal gills develop, and finally, about the time the front legs appear, gills are

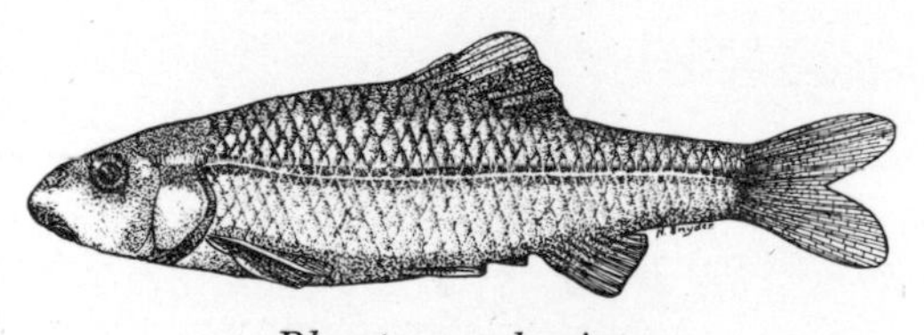

Blunt-nosed minnow

Black crappie

replaced by lungs. When feeding, newts should be removed from the aquarium and placed in a small dish of water containing tiny pieces of raw meat, tiny earthworms, mealworms, or minced shellfish, or prepared fish foods. As a rule, the salamanders and turtles should be separated from fishes in a aquarium as

The yellow, or blue, angel fish is a hardy aquarium species

they are apt to bite the fishes' tails. The small green turtles sold in pet shops need a rock on which they can climb out of the water. They can be fed in the same manner as the newts.

The Saltwater Aquarium

The salt water aquarium is equally interesting and anyone wishing to establish one will find detailed information in Clifford B. Moore's *The Book of Wild Pets*, Charles T. Branford Company, publishers, New York. Marine aquaria are rather difficult to maintain but anyone willing to meet the requirements will be richly rewarded.

The unfamiliar world that exists under water holds a great fascination for the curious-minded of all ages. It is a strange and varied world. Although the number of species of creatures living in water is now less than the number of species of land animals, life originated in the sea. There it evolved into a great number of types, some of which advanced into fresh water and others onto land. Freshwater life has not all come directly from the sea. Some of the plants and animals have gone back to water after a period of land life. All forms have made interesting adaptations and it is possible to explore fresh water life for years without exhausting its surprises and its interest.

—A.K.B.

Recommended Reading

Along the Brook—Raymond T. Fuller. John Day Company, New York.
An Aquarium—Glens O. Blough. Row, Peterson and Company, New York.
Beginner's Guide to Fresh-Water Life—Leon A. Houseman. G. P. Putnam's Sons, New York.
Beginner's Guide to Seashore Life—Leon A. Houseman. G. P. Putnam's Sons, New York.
Exotic Aquarium Fishes—William T. Innes. Innes Publishing Company, Philadelphia.
Field Book of Ponds and Streams—Ann H. Morgan. G. P. Putnam's Sons, New York.
Freshwater Fishes of the World—Guenther Sterba. The Viking Press, New York.
Goldfish Varieties and Water Gardens—William T. Innes. Innes Publishing Co., Philadelphia.
Guide to Higher Aquarium Animals—Edward T. Boardman. Cranbrook Institute of Science, Bloomfield Hills, Michigan.
Handbook of Tropical Aquarium Fishes—Herbert R. Axelrod and Leonard P. Schultz. McGraw-Hill Book Company, Inc., New York.
Turtox Service Leaflets published by General Biological Supply House, 8200 So. Hoyne Ave., Chicago 20, Illinois. No. 5, Starting and Maintaining a Balanced Fresh-Water Aquarium.

AQUATIC INSECT (*See under Insect: Insects of Ponds and Streams*)

ARANSAS NATIONAL WILDLIFE REFUGE

Location—Coastal Texas
Size—74 square miles
Mammals—Collared peccaries, armadillos, raccoons, opossums, deer, squirrels
Birdlife—Whooping cranes, sandhill cranes, turkeys, herons, caracaras, white-tailed hawks; in winter, ducks and geese of many species; hosts of songbirds in migration
Plants—Salt marsh plants, coastal oak forests

The salt marshes along the coast give way to rolling sand hills with low forest of oaks. This is the winter home of one of the world's rarest birds, the whooping crane. The collared peccary, an animal related to the pigs, is protected here.

Accommodations – Facilities are available at Rockport, about 33 miles from the refuge
Headquarters—On the refuge, at Austwell, Texas

Whooping cranes from Canada winter in Aransas National Wildlife Refuge, Texas

ARBORVITAE
American Arborvitae
Other Common Names—Northern white cedar
Scientific Name—*Thuja occidentalis*
Family—Pinaceae (pine family)
Range—Eastern Quebec to Saskatchewan, south to Nova Scotia, northern and western New England and New York, limestone areas of mountains south to Tennessee, North Carolina, Ohio, northern Indiana, northeastern Illinois, Wisconsin and Minnesota
Habitat—Essentially a tree of the cold, humid North; in swamps and stream margins
Leaves—Flat sprays consisting of four rows of flat, scalelike leaves arranged in a chainlike pattern. These are lighter green below and each scale in the center row has a small studlike gland. Not prickly to the touch like some cedars
Bark—Thin, rather light yellowish-gray or orange-brown on the surface, redder beneath. Not so shreddy as other cedars; older trunks show a tendency to narrow, interlacing ridges
Flowers—Very inconspicuous and small —April or May
Fruit—Upright pod-shaped cones somewhat less than one-half inch long, born in groups on outer twigs. Yellow-green, ripening in autumn to tawny and chestnut tones, when they open their petal scales to release tiny winged seeds

Arborvitae, *Thuja occidentalis*, often called American arborvitae, has one relative, *Thuja plicata*, called giant arborvitae, an important lumber tree of the western United States. Besides these two there are a number of arborvitaes from the Orient that are used, along with the native American arborvitae, for landscaping. These have been developed by horticulturists to produce a number or varieties with pronounced characteristics such as fan-shaped foliage and varied foliage colors.

The native American arborvitae is quite different in appearance from most nursery arborvitae stock and attains a fair size in the northern cold swamps, moist pastures, and stream and pond banks where it grows wild.

American arborvitae

Occasional trees may exceed 50 or 60 feet in height with trunk diameters up to three feet or more. At a distance the foliage often seems very dense, but at close range one usually finds that most of it is confined to the ends of the rather short branches and has a clipped feathery appearance. There is none of the prickly texture that is typical of the foliage of two other eastern trees, red cedar, *Juniperus virginiana*, and the coastal white cedar, *Chamaecyparis thyoides*. The arborvitae leaves are flat, small, rounded and scalelike, and arranged in

a chainlike fashion on the twigs. Also, the small, pod-shaped cones easily separate it from the other cedars.

American arborvitae, like the more southern *Chamaecyparis*, has a wood that is famed for its durability in water. It is used for canoes, larger craft, tubs and barrels, floats, fenceposts and shingles. The big western arborvitae, *Thuja plicata*, has a wood of reddish brown that finds a wide variety of uses, from cigar boxes to large timbers and dock pilings. Its tough, stringy easily peeled bark has been used for making baskets, rope, and cordage. —M.H.B.

Giant Arborvitae
Other Common Names— Western red cedar, canoe cedar and Pacific red cedar
Scientific Name— *Thuja plicata*
Family— Pinaceae (pine family)
Range—The Pacific Coast region from southeastern Alaska to western British Columbia, western Washington, western Oregon, and northwestern California; eastward in the Rocky Mountains from eastern Washington, northern Idaho, and western Montana, north to southeastern British Columbia

The Moose Creek Arborvitae

Arborvitae, a Latin name, means "Tree of life." It is an appropriate name for one of the hardiest and longest-lived trees on the North American continent.

Arborvitaes of Moose Creek, Idaho, and other places of the West, are also called cedars, and more generally, western red cedars, but they are true *Thuja*, with the typical small cones, the rich balsam smell, the soft light weight, but extremely tough and water resistant wood, and the many flattened branchlets.

The arborvitaes of Moose Creek are a luxuriant grove, covering some 500 acres, the last remaining survivors of what was once an extensive forest. That so many survive is due to the fact that they are truly a tree of life, and they are so far removed from the lumberman's axe.

Giant arborvitae grove at Moose Creek, Idaho

These trees stand in the deep recesses of America's largest wilderness area, the Bitterroot-Selway Area of Montana and Idaho. Here approximately 1,600,000 acres have been set aside as primeval wilderness, and commercial exploitation cannot enter in. The big arborvitaes are one proof of why it is necessary to have such large areas set aside as wilderness.

Moose Creek is an important feeder stream for the Selway River, a part of the Columbia River system. It gets its start in the lofty, rugged Bitterroot Mountains, and flows some 50 miles before it empties into the Selway. Approximately five miles up from its mouth begin its two major branches, the east and west forks. The big arborvitaes are along the east branch of the creek, 14 miles from the mouth, slightly beyond an old trapper's cabin used by the U.S. Forest Service as a temporary guard station.

The Moose Creek country has been hard hit by fires in the past. It was swept by the gigantic blaze that burned over so much of northern Idaho in 1910, including the towns of Wallace and Kellogg. Again, in 1934, the large fire that started on Pete King Creek to the west swept through the country. Other years have seen other fires burning over smaller areas, but no less destructive for the area they did burn. It does seem remarkable that such a large grove of virgin trees could remain in fine health after such a prolonged series of fires. One can view this grove and reflect what

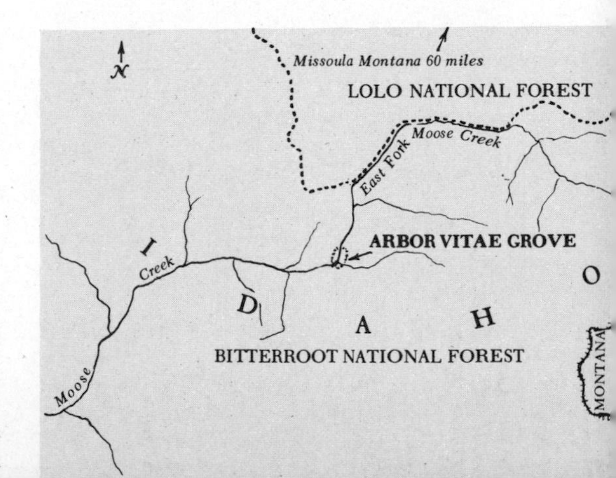

that vast Selway country must have been like before the fires swept through it.

Although fires here have destroyed millions of fine trees that represent billions of feet of vital timber, they have had at least one good effect. They have created some of the finest elk country in the United States. And when one reflects that just north of here, in the Clearwater Country, the Lewis and Clark expedition had its roughest time and had to butcher its horses to survive, he can better appreciate the conditions that have caused the elk to populate the area in such vast numbers. The Selway herd alone has been estimated at some 14,000 elk, a lot of elk even when they are scattered over some two million acres.

The series of fires have also given the shrubs a better chance to grow—plants like ceanothus, or deer brush, Oregon grape snowberry, and serviceberry. The elk and deer find these palatable, especially during the winter when the heavy snow affords them little else to feed on. Big game does not thrive in a mature, dense forest land, for the very reason that some of these shrubs do not grow readily under the thick canopy of mature timber.

Arborvitaes are not the only mature trees left standing in this area. For, though fires may sweep clean in the path they follow, they do take a crooked path, following the lines of least resistance, carried along by the wind or their own draft, and isolating pockets of timber here and there. Man, too, helped in the Selway country by throwing his battle lines in front of the flames, saving patches of timber here and there. Even though he could not overcome the fire entirely, he could change its course or hold it off when he could muster enough strength to do so. More than 5,000 men fought the Pete King fire in 1934, and though it burned briskly until the last day of September when the fall rains finally let down in a torrent, this force of men was sufficient to beat down the inferno in strategic places, leaving virgin timber still standing. Some of this timber is still here today—magnificent yellow-pine stands. Douglas fir, the stream-loving spruces, some larch, and what lodgepole pine the beetles did not get during the insect-infested 1930's.

Even on the brightest day there is a twilight mood in the midst of the arborvitaes. A cypress swamp has often been described as a gloomy place, but one could not say this about an arborvitae grove. There, the rich balsam smell, the springiness underfoot, and the sunlight slanting through the canopy overhead, lighting up the otherwise dark interior, give one a feeling of cheerfulness and well being.

These great trees, the largest of which are 8 to 10 feet in diameter, and from 150 to 200 feet tall, were thriving even before the white man first set foot on this continent. They make mere man feel small under their great shadows.

Though the arborvitaes are more fire resistant than are most trees, they are not fireproof. No tree is fireproof, probably not even the cypress, to which the arborvitae is related. There is plenty of evidence that the arborvitae is killed by fire, for in the lower reaches of the creek, below Elbow Bend, great monarchs stand gaunt and naked, the snags left from the 1910 inferno.

All the way down Moose Creek these dead trees can be found, with a few live trees still standing that had resisted the fire miraculously enough. Though fire had killed many trees, they were also standing, nearly 40 years after they had died, and many of these will still be standing years from now, so slow are they to rot, and so firmly entrenched are they against the wind. When one of these monarchs falls, the sound rings a long time in one's ears. Even the fallen trees survive many years before they begin to decay. One can occasionally find other trees, several feet in diameter, growing astride the fallen ones.

Like its relative the American arbor-

A scene at Moose Creek, Idaho, with Bailey Mountain in the background

vitae, the western arborvitae prefers a moist area in which to grow. They are usually found along the streams, or in the shady, moist dells where there are springs and sometimes swampy conditions.

In the fall it is easy to gain the impression that these trees are dying, for then the branchlets are a reddish brown. The older branchlets die and drop off after two or three years; but there are new, green branchlets to take their places. The cones, too, add to this impression, for they are russet-brown when they mature and shed their seeds in late August; and they drop from the tree the following spring. They are very small for a tree so large, being only one-third to one-half inch long. The snow stays late in the Moose Creek country, and in the late spring thousands of arborvitae cones can be seen scattered over its surface.

The bark of the tree, too, is interesting, and quite distinctive. It is a cinnamon-brown, and thin and stringy, and is useful for tanning. It is said that the leaves have a medicinal value.

Unlike its neighbors, the yellow pines, the arborvitaes do not readily shed their lower branches. These are retained, and they add to the tree's majestic appearance, sweeping outward and downward as they do in a long arch, giving the tree grace and symmetry. It is not hard to believe that the arborvitaes may be related to the giant sequoias of California. Some of them even rival the sequoias in size.

The arborvitaes have been given another name which seems appropriate. They are sometimes called *canoe cedars.* They got this name because the Indians hollowed out the trunks to make their canoes, some of them 60 feet long. These trees must make fine canoes, for the wood is light, and very buoyant in the water. The Indians had other uses for the arborvitaes: they used the planks to build their lodges, they carved their totem poles from the easily worked wood, and they used the fibrous inner bark for making ropes and coarse blankets.

It is good to know that the Moose Creek arborvitaes are protected from commercial exploitation, for they are a fine stand, one of the finest remaining anywhere. There are many uses for these trees in the commercial world. At Christmas-time they are in demand, because their pressed, needled branches make lovely wreaths and decorations. The Moose Creek grove stands many miles from the lumberman's axe. There are no roads through that country. The nearest road is 20 miles away, and the nearest town, Hamilton, Montana, is 50 miles away.

The Moose Creek arborvitaes are safe and are thriving. Only fire could harm them, and fires are unlikely because the fire organization that protects the Moose Creek country is better equipped to prevent tragic fires, like the Pete King, from occurring again. From the lonely sentinel on the lookout tower to the helicopter-flying smoke chasers, the Forest Service is prepared to take action at the first sign of trouble. With this aid, the Moose Creek arborvitaes should live for many more centuries, preserving for man a dignity and grace unsurpassed by any tree anywhere. —M.K.B.

ARBOVIRUS

Arbovirus is the abbreviation for arthropod-borne-virus, a term used in public health work for virus diseases which are transmitted by insects and related arthropods. Equine encephalitis is the best-known arbovirus disease in the United States. —R.C.C.

ARCHES NATIONAL MONUMENT

Location—Southeastern Utah
Size—54 square miles in five areas
Mammals—Cougars, deer, coyotes, foxes
Birdlife—Red-tailed hawks, Say's Phoebes, Brewer's sparrows
Plants—Cacti and many desert flowers such as larkspurs, lupines, desert mallows, pentstemons

The Entrada Sandstone, a 300-foot thick deposit of red rock, was cracked by geological forces. Water, leaching into these cracks, dissolved the weak sandstone, eventually leaving huge walls of rock standing at some distance from one another. Freezing, thawing, and wind-driven grains of sand all had a part in the formation of the individual walls and of the arches cut into the softer rock near the base. There are 81 arches in all stages of formation within the monument.

Accommodations—None at the monument; the closest town is Moab
Headquarters—Five miles north of Moab, Utah

ARCTIC-ALPINE
Wildlife at Timberline

At timberline on the highest mountains of North America, where the earthborn forest and the skyborn fury of the elements vie for control, every tree shows the violence of battle. Some crouch forward, hugging the rocks and the bleached trunks of their ancestors, others reel backward, their growing tips thrashing downwind like corn tassels. Some form little societies, intertwining their branches and making a stand together, and others lie prone and spread out until they are not trees at all but mere mats of ground cover. Botanically these timberline trees differ in no way from the tall limber pine specimens of the valleys, in appearance they are a race apart—gnarled, dwarfed, and dedicated to fighting.

Arches National Monument

Depending upon its distance north of the equator, timberline may vary from sea level upward to 12,000 feet or more. In the temperate zone, the strongest element controlling the heights to which timberline may reach seems to be wind. The wind is king above the line. In the marginland of struggle it is wind and windborne ice crystals that together sandblast the bark of standing trees; it is wind that saws off the tips of the low-lying trees when they grow up past the protective level of rocks and snowdrifts. Isolated Mount Washington in New Hampshire, with its high-wind velocities, has a timberline that dips to 4,000 feet above the sea, but in the Rocky Mountains of Colorado timber grows up to altitudes of 11,500 feet.

Lack of soil, poor drainage, snowfields and forest fires also have a hand in dictating the ups and downs of the tree-growing level. Research may dis-

Foxtail pines struggle to survive at timberline in the central Rocky Mountains

close that the season of ground-thaw and the depth of the thawing may also have an important influence upon tree growth at timberline.

In the mountains there is little to show that timberline has any tendency to move up or down. Where there is only dead timber, it is traceable to fire. Where there is only young timber, there is usually evidence of old burns.

In the Far North it is the distance northward rather than height above sea level that sets the timberline. There the forest does not generally have its fringe of gnarled and weather-hammered veterans. Trees have been successfully grown some distance north of the timberline, and evidence from pollen-preserving peat bogs there indicates that trees are marching northward into new terrain.

Timberline trees are conifers of several kinds. Sometimes spruces, pines, and firs will all be found in the same area. The firs and occasionally the spruces can grow into circular thickets that are like atolls. This happens when the branches on the ground put out roots of their own and so surround the mother tree with a ring of fresh growth.

Some spruce trees show a faster growth rate at timberline than in the competitive forest below. Where there are several types of trees in a front line, it is the spruces that are the advance scouts. They can hold any little hollow in the ground, shaping themselves to it with what looks like a trunkless mass of greenery.

Pines (in the central Rockies they are foxtail pines) are the heavyweights of the fighting line. They have a way of sending out living and growing branches on their lea sides long after the bark has been wind-battered from their windward sides. Ring-counted specimens not far below timberline show an age of 1,800 years.

The vertical depth of the timberline battlefield occasionally runs to 500 feet, if the depth is considered to be from the first dwarfed trees to the last shrub-type trees that hide away high on the

Caribou cross a high alpine meadow in Mount McKinley National Park, Alaska

High above timberline where spring and summer are brief, wild flowers appear in great numbers and complete their reproduction processes rapidly

slopes. The break between straight, normal trees and low, crooked ones is often quite distinct, but it is rarely even. On the smooth west face of Pike's Peak there is a stretch of a mile or two that looks as level as a mapper's contour line. This is rare, even on a mountainside with no draws and ridges. Normally the warfront is as jagged and toothed as the individual trees which maintain it.

When the battle rages, the thick, matted trees of timberline often give shelter to high-country birds, which seek their branches for protection.

Ruby-crowned kinglets inhabit spruce-fir forests

Few bird species nest in the dwarf evergreens, though the eastern ruby-crowned kinglets sometimes hang a nest between the forked evergreen limbs and gray-headed juncos nest on the ground underneath them. MacGillivray's and pileolated warblers, which in high country nest up to four feet above the ground, prefer alpine willows to pines.

The white-crowned sparrow chooses bushes or the ground, often nesting above timberline. In Colorado this bird is confined to the mountains during the breeding season, but in fall it descends to lower levels where it mixes with the Gambel's sparrow, a regular migrant in eastern Colorado.

Other bird highlanders are the rosy finches which nest in steep cliffs at and above timberline.

Winter drives these finches down the mountains, but not away from them, and they often forage in the large, open, grass parks at 8,000 or 9,000 feet. Flocks of them follow the snowplows and the ski area bulldozers to get the weed seeds that are exposed.

The Rocky Mountain pipit consistently breeds above timberline, incubating its eggs in little grass cups between the rocks. White-tailed ptarmigans invariably nest above timberline. Considering their size—they are small grouse, 12 inches long—they are the best camouflaged of all the highland birds. In winter their plumage is snow-white, and in summer it is so wonderfully like the millions of stones set in the grass all around that one discovers pipits only by the shadow that moves along beneath them as they walk about. Summer or winter, they are loath to fly. When an intruder comes within 10 or 12 feet of them, the birds usually walk off, stepping quickly from tuft to tuft, but hesitating between steps.

Smaller birds tend to fly low and cautiously above timberline. Watching them one has the impression they are fearful of gusts of wind that will catch them from beneath and fling them far out before they can come in for a landing. With any breeze stirring they make their flights in short dips and hops.

Birds that nest well below timberline often drift up to timberline after their young leave the nest. Red-tailed hawks and prairie falcons sometimes follow the rising spring tide as it advances up the slopes. One observer has even seen a marsh hawk riding the air currents over Pike's Peak though this bird's nesting area is on the prairie far below. Golden eagles are usually visitors at timberline, although one Colorado nest has been found 400 feet above timberline.

On Pike's Peak the upper air watcher will sometimes see dozens of ravens flying together over their nests among the rock crevices.

Timberline birds have mammalian company, too. Woodchucks, under the highland alias of marmots, lumber about everywhere. There is the coney, a little rabbit-shaped creature which ducks deep among the rocks and sends up muffled squeaks as one passes above it. Campers, tempted by the shelter of deserted mine shacks, learn about the pack rat which picks up anything small enough for it to handle and carries it off to its nest.

These small timberline rodents attract the red fox, the bobcat, and occasionally the prairie-going coyote into the uplands. At one time or another one may see them slink in and out of the timberline forest border.

Timberline also shelters elk, which at night like to graze their way up into the grassy draws and meadows. Deer also

White-tailed ptarmigans nest in high alpine meadows above timberline

Mountain sheep inhabit the rocky cliffs high in western mountains.

like the high country and browse among the scrub trees and still higher, where the visitor might be straining his eyes for the sight of bighorn sheep.

Curious and interesting is a tiny form of timberline life so small that most people would not suspect that it was a living plant. An algae, *Sphaerella*, this primitive growth causes an extraordinary pinkness on the timberline snow.

In summer the mountain tops above timberline are gay with alpine flowers and bird notes. The wild, twisted trees, now in peaceful repose, show the ravages of a violence that has come and gone. But if you visit them in winter when the wind is on the warpath, you may wonder how they have survived the wild tempests at timberline.

ARMADILLO
Nine-banded Armadillo
Other Common Names—Armored pig
Scientific Name—*Dasypus novemcinctus*
Family—Dasypodidae (armadillos)
Order—Edentata
Size—Body length, 15 to 17 inches; tail, 14 to 16 inches; weight, 9 to 15 pounds
Range—Texas, Oklahoma, and eastern Mississippi, south through Mexico, Central America, and Argentina; introduced into Florida

The armadillo is not likely to be confused with any other animal in the United States. With a chunky body, short stubby legs, and naked mulelike ears, it is the only mammal in this country that is armored from the end of its sharp snout to the tip of the long trailing tail.

A flat bony plate covers the front of the head, and the body is almost as thoroughly encased in a shell like that of a tortoise. The covering forms a solid curved arch on the back above the fore and hind legs, but movable hooplike sections cover the center of the body. These central sections give it the appearance of being striped or banded and there are variable numbers of them in different species of armadillos.

It is difficult to distinguish between the sexes in armadillos because males and females are so similar in appearand and habits. The armadillos mate in July or August.

Unlike humans who give birth to quadruplets once in approximately 7 million, the armadillos have quadruplets at almost every birth. Only rarely are as many as five or as few as two or three born. Most amazing, the youngsters are

The nine-banded armadillo feeds almost entirely on insects

identical quadruplets. Embryological studies show that each batch of four is the result of a single fertilized egg which divides twice. Each of the four resulting cells then develops into a miniature armadillo which is born in early spring some six months after the adults have mated. All members of a single brood are of the same sex. Young armadillos have their shell covering complete, but it remains soft until they become adults, thus allowing for growth.

The armadillo usually makes its home in a branching burrow which it easily digs in the ground with its long front claws. The length of the burrow varies from a few to many feet and the opening is six to eight inches in diameter. When the digging is completed the female gathers leaves and grasses that she carries underground and constructs a crude nest in the slightly enlarged end of the burrow. There she spends the hottest parts of the day in relative safety and comfort. There, too, occurs the birth of the identical quadruplets. The female suckles her youngsters with milk from her mammary glands until the infants are strong enough to follow her on food-hunting expeditions. The quads remain with their mother for two or three months and then they gradually drift away to build burrows for themselves and to take up the responsibilities and risks of adult life.

The word *armadillo* is the Spanish diminutive of *armado,* meaning armed. Armadillos have been called armored pigs, and in their foraging for food they do resemble pigs.

Approximately 80 percent of their food consists of insects, such as sugarcane borers, termites, ground beetles, fire ants, wireworms, cockroaches, centipedes, fly larvae, and grasshoppers. The diet also includes blackberries, mulberries, and occasionally, eggs and other animals.

Many insects are discovered as the armadillo plows furrows through soft soil with its nose, often giving vent to an occasional piglike grunt. Ants are a favorite food and if a nest is discovered, the armadillo's long, sticky tongue darts rapidly back and forth, licking up hordes of the scrambling insects (*See also under Anteater*).

Armadillos are primarily night prowlers, although it is not unusual to see them in early morning or late afternoon. Neither their sense of sight nor sense of hearing is well developed. Consequently it is often possible to approach closely to a foraging armadillo. When alarmed it runs off with amazing speed. Dodging rapidly back and forth, it heads for a nearby burrow.

The armadillo is an expert digger and if its retreat is cut off it is quite likely to decide that it had better go underground. Digging furiously with the large claws on its front feet, an adult literally sinks from the sight of an astonished observer. Once fully buried, the frightened armadillo hangs on to the sides of the burrow until the danger has passed.

Human beings, coyotes, foxes, and all flesh-eating animals are numbered among the armadillo's enemies. Its shell furnishes a certain amount of protection, but it cannot make as efficient use of its hard coat as can some of its South American relatives, whose "shells" cover them so completely that by rolling themselves up into a rounded armored ball they discourage all except the most persistent attackers.

The nine-banded armadillo is not so well protected and, when danger threatens, it beats a hasty retreat. Its defensive weapons—long claws and scent glands—are not very effective against most enemies.

Some people eat armadillos, and the meat is said to have a slightly porklike taste. But the armor or the small shelled animal is probably a greater attraction to mercenary human beings than is the flesh. Baskets made from the shells are standard sale items in many curio stores in the Southwest.

Until about 1870, armadillos were known to live only in the lower Rio Grande Valley of Texas, within the United States. Since then they have slowly spread north and east, and now they are in Texas, Oklahoma, Arkansas, and across the southern states to Florida. Much of this migration was presumably done by the armadillo itself, but the escape of pets from captivity and deliberate introductions may have helped.

Although the armadillo is in some respects a hardy animal, it is probable that it has now reached the northern limits of its range. It does not hibernate, and extended freezes kill off its food supply so that adventurous northern migrants often starve or are frozen to death as they search for food. Extensive droughts kill great numbers of them, and therefore armadillos are less numerous, or absent, in dry regions. (*See also under Mammal*) —O.P.B.

ARROWHEAD

Broad-leaved Arrowhead
Other Common Names—Wapato, duck-potato
Scientific Name—*Sagittaria latifolia*
Family—Alismataceae (water-plantain family)
Range—North America except in the extreme north
Habitat—Edges of ponds, lakes, and marshes
Time of Blooming—July through September

During the summer, the waxy, three-petaled white flowers of this plant decorate the edges of many ponds, marshes, and streams. The flowering stalk rises out of the water, sometimes as much as a foot, and bears several flowers at its summit.

The flowers are unisexual and occur in whorls of three, with the less attractive and inconspicuous female flowers forming the lower whorls. On the up-

Broad-leaved arrowhead

per part of the stalk are borne the male flowers, comprising a center of golden stamens surrounded by three white petals. Insects are attracted first to the more conspicuous male flowers, with pollination occurring later as the female flowers are visited.

A variety of insects carry the pollen of the arrowhead. The majority are insects common to wet places, among them the large-winged dragonfly.

The leaves of the plant stand erect and are sometimes confused with those of the pickerelweed. However, basal lobes of arrowhead leaves are long-pointed while those of the pickerelweed are rounded. The two commonly intermingle as their soil and water requirements seem to be the same.

Arrowhead leaves are clearly arrow-shaped, but occur in different natural forms. These forms include broad as well as lance-shaped leaf blades, with linear and sagittate forms also found. In general, leaves borne beneath the water in this aquatic plant are linear and grasslike since a broad blade would not remain intact in water currents. Leaves borne above the water, on the other hand, are broad-shaped, giving greater photosynthetic efficiency.

The tuberous starchy roots of the various members of this genus have long been important articles of food to the Chinese and to the North American Indians. Early settlers learned of it from the Indians and called it swamp potato. In 1805 when Lewis and Clark made their explorative trip down the Columbia River, they saw the Indian women wading in the swamps and harvesting the tubers of arrowhead by breaking them off with their toes.

Both the fruits and tubers are eaten by waterfowl, and the tubers are consumed by ducks. More than 16 species of ducks and geese are known to feed on these plants.

The arrowheads are considered modern representatives of an ancestral stock of the monocotyledons, or plants with one seed leaf. Belonging to the water-plantain family, the arrowheads are represented by some 75 species, including the broadleaf form described above as well as the lance-leaf and long-beaked forms that grow in swamps. —A.M.M.

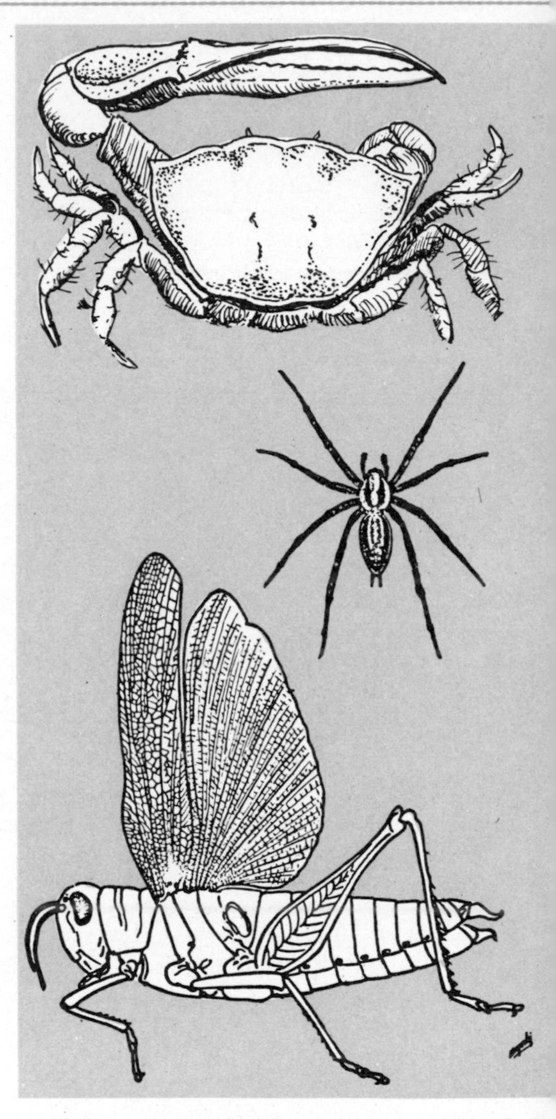

Fiddler crab (top); grass, or funnel spider (center); and grasshopper (bottom) are representative of the diverse Arthropod phylum

ARTHROPOD

The Arthropoda is a phylum of the animal kingdom (*see Animal: Animal Kingdom*), one of 30 of these great divisions. It contains approximately four-fifths of all known species of animals. Its members, spiders, crustaceans, and insects, wear the skeleton on the outside of the body (exoskeleton), and have jointed legs. The name of the phylum is a combination of the Greek words for joint and for foot.

The ancestors of the arthropods were segmented marine worms, whose unspecialized segments gradually modified under evolutionary pressures into structures of great and increasing variety. One major branch of the phylum developed antennae; the insects and the crustaceans belong to this subphylum, the Antennata. The other subphylum, the Chelicerata, lacks these appendages; among its living representatives are the spiders, the scorpions, and the horseshoe crab. (*See Horseshoe Crab*)

The shell of the arthropod is formed from secretions of the tissues directly under it which are deposited in layers. The three substances are *chitin,* which is perhaps the most important, and *selerotin* and *cuticulin.* They combine to producc a tough, resistant material that offcrs efficient protection against bacterial invasion, desiccation, and chemical action.

When first formed, the exoskeleton is usually almost colorless and soft, but it soon hardens and darkens. When fully firmed, it cannot be expanded without cracking; therefore, all growing arthropods must molt the shell and replace it with a larger one. Some of the marine arthropods, such as crabs and lobsters, reinforce the chitin of the shell with calcium carbonate (lime).

A great number of terrestrial arthropods in the class Insecta are winged. These attachments are actually extensions of the body wall, as opposed to the wings of birds and of bats, which are modified limbs (*See* ***under Bird. Bird Flight***).

Arthropods have a simplified circulatory system, and their blood is usually colorless or pale yellow. They have no respiratory systems corresponding to the muscle-powered lungs of the vertebrates. Terrestrial (land) arthropods obtain oxygen through the molecular diffusion of gases, a system that is efficient only for rather small life forms; this one factor, more than any other, limits their size. Aquatic arthropods may have internal gills, as do crabs, or external gill books, as in horseshoe crabs.

—G.B.S.

White ash (above); poison sumac (below)

ASH

White Ash

Other Common Names—American ash, Biltmore ash

Scientific Name—*Fraxinus americana*

Family—Oleaceae (olive family)

Range—Nova Scotia and Maine to south-central Minnesota; south to east Texas and northern Florida

Habitat—Favors rich woodland soils

Leaves—Compound, about a foot long with five to nine (usually seven) oval leaflets, pale beneath and set well away from the center stem. Leaflets vary in shape but the last pair are always smaller than the rest; in autumn they

turn to clear yellow and plum
Bark—Smooth, rather tan when young, splitting to form diamond-shaped grooves between a network of raised areas, cross-checked on older trees
Flowers—The male blossoms are often most noticeable, appearing on separate trees just before the leaves open. They are stubby, brushlike clumps with dark purplish anthers
Fruit—Hanging sprays of narrow, winged seeds, one to two inches long

There are more than a half dozen kinds of ash in the eastern United States and the country-wide count, including varieties, runs to about 20. Many of these are so similar to each other that even tree experts must check them carefully to separate them. The chief differences are in the breadth and proportions of leaves and seeds, and in details of the winter buds.

White ash is one of the more common and widely distributed varieties, being recognized as a superb shade tree. It grows both in and at the edges of deep forests and is most common in small woodland clearings and along roadsides where, in the autumn, the pale yellow, peach-tan, and lavender-tinted leaves contrast with the more gaudy oak and maple foliage. A glance at the noticeably opposite-branched arrangement of twigs and limbs will help to distinguish the ash from the somewhat similar hickories.

The ash is in great demand as timber. The hard, strong wood, while not quite so heavy as oak or hickory, is only slightly inferior to the hickory for tool handles, etc., and possibly superior to it for some uses. One expert notes a maximum tree height of 120 feet with a six-foot trunk diameter but a good-sized average tree may not be much more than half these dimensions. Some of the biggest ones living today have been preserved in the yards of old country churches and inns.

The spear-head shaped, winged, seeds go spiralling off in the wind when ripe, sometimes sticking into soft soil point-first when they land, ready to grow. On male trees the remains of the dried blossoms may stay up on the upper branches throughout the fall, making the bare trees recognizable at some distance.

Quaking aspen

Oddly, one small tree or shrub with whose leaves young ash trees are sometimes easily confused is the poison sumac, *Rhus vernix*. Poison sumacs usually show more pairs of leaflets on each compound stem, which is red, at least on the upper surface. A picture of its foliage is shown below that of white ash in the illustration. —M.H.B.

ASPEN

Quaking Aspen

Other Common Names—Trembling poplar

Scientific Name—*Populus tremuloides*

Family—Salicaceae (willow family)

Range—From Newfoundland to Alaska, south to Connecticut and Iowa, the Dakotas, parts of Nebraska; also on moist, cool, upland slopes west into Mexico

Habitat—Grows most abundantly where coniferous forest and grasslands meet; forms extensive groves at higher altitudes in the West, particularly on burned-over forest areas

Leaves—Small, 1½ to 3 inches across, almost circular, usually with a short point and with fine, rounded, marginal teeth. The stem (petiole) is long and flattened, allowing the blade to bounce and rotate in the wind. Leaf color is golden yellow in autumn. Winter leaf buds are small, pointed, and shiny

Bark—Smooth, tight, and pale yellow to chalky-green, marked at junctions with branches by rough, blackish seams. Dark areas sometimes cover much of the lower trunk on older trees

Flowers—Male: stout, rough pussies that grow into longer, fuzzier catkins. Female: like the small cottonwood tassels

Fruit—It produces a silky, seed-bearing fluff

The rather long, flattened stems of aspen leaves give them such freedom of motion that even the smallest winds cause them to turn and flutter twinkling in the breeze. This trait, shared in some degree by many of the poplars, may serve to protect the rather delicate foliage against the effects of hot sun during dry, windy weather. Many, if not all of this family of trees have a rather northerly range or prefer higher altitudes.

Aspen grows in greatest profusion in the West and in Canada, often in extensive groves where there is sufficient ground water. Usually they are associated with evergreen forests. Their pale, creamy, green trunks, and, in autumn, their bright yellow foliage, show up in vivid contrast against dark green backgrounds. If one is not familiar with the species one might think they were white birches, but the smooth bark has warmer colors and usually shows more rough dark areas of the old bark advancing up the trunk from ground level.

In winter the bark colors, and straight, vertical trunks stand out, and it can be easily separated from other trees of this group by its sharp, shiny, dark brown buds.

In spring, these buds become soft, fuzzy rust-and-gray catkins soon followed by the white-fuzzed young leaves.

At all seasons it is an attractive tree, a worthy addition to private grounds as well as to wild forests. However, the poplar family is a water-hungry group whose roots may clog drain pipes and sewers. —M.H.B.

ASTER

New England Aster

Other Common Names—Common aster

Scientific Name—*Aster novae-angliae*

Family—Compositae (composite family)

Range—Quebec to South Carolina, west to Colorado

Habitat—Fields

Time of Blooming—August to frost time

Heath Aster

Other Common Names—Michaelmas daisy, frost-weed

Scientific Name—*Aster ericoides*

Family—Compositae (composite family)

Range—Throughout eastern United States, west to South Dakota, north to Manitoba, and south to New Mexico and Texas

Habitat—Dry open places

Time of Blooming—July to October

Among the autumn-blooming wild flowers the wild asters vie with the goldenrods for first place. Many species

New England aster

of asters dominate the roadsides and open woods in autumn.

Asters abound throughout the eastern half of the United States, spreading their range west to Colorado and north into Canada.

Taken from the Greek, *Aster* means star and was so named because of its starlike floral heads. There are more than 200 known kinds of asters in North America. They belong to the great family of composites, which are characterized by tight-packed or compound flower heads. Asters, like many members of the composite family, are usually characterized by brilliantly colored ray flowers arranged around a common center or disk of tiny tubular flowers.

Largely dependent upon insects for cross pollination, the asters furnish an abundance of nectar for their insect visitors, honeybees, bumblebees, and flowerflies. The tiny dry seeds of the asters have tufts of hair which, like parachutes, are blown about by the wind far from the parent plants.

Because their characteristics are so similar, many of the species are difficult to identify; however, a few common species can be distinguished by observing where they grow, the shape and texture of the leaves, the manner of branching, and the color and size of the flowers. The colors range from deep purple through violet, lavender, and blue to white.

For identification purposes, the asters can be divided into two groups: the purple-blue group and the white-flowered group.

Purple-Blue Asters

New England aster, *Aster novae-angliae*

This common, but handsome, wild aster is a tall, stout, branching plant with very dark purple or occasionally pinkish flowers. The leaves, which are lance-shaped, and stemless, clasp the stem. The New England aster blooms in moist open ground from August until November. A widely cultivated plant, it is often used in gardens. Horticulturists have developed several different color variations with longer ray flowers.

New York aster, *Aster novi-belgii*

The New York aster, a tall slender

plant growing in swampy places, is common along the Atlantic Coast. A late-flowering species, it ranges in color from bluish-violet to bluish-white. Its light green leaves are lance-shaped and entirely or slightly toothed.

Late Purple aster, *Aster patens*
Often called spreading aster or rough-leaved wood aster, this species grows in dry places and can be recognized by its slender, widely branched rough stem. The showy purplish-blue flowers grow at the ends of wiry branches. The rough leaves are oblong and clasp the stem.

Purple-stemmed aster, *Aster puniceus*
Very common in swampy places, this species is tall with a rough, hairy, usually purplish, stem and large purple flowers. The rough, oval, long-pointed leaves clasp the stem. Very often it blooms a second time, late in the fall; then, its flowers are larger and darker than early in the season, as is usually the case with late-blooming plants.

Smooth aster, *Aster laevis*
This common violet-blue aster is found growing in dry, open places such as roadsides and the borders of woods, and especially on open hillsides. Its stout smooth stem is covered with smooth ovate leaves.

Stiff-leaved aster, *Aster linariifolius*
This small plant has very pretty large violet-blue flowers, a short, stiff stem and narrow, rough, stiff leaves. It occurs in some dry, sandy places.

Blue wood aster, *Aster cordifolius*
The blue wood aster, sometimes called heart-shaped aster, is a tall bushy plant with toothed, heart-shaped and long petioled lower leaves; the upper leaves are sessile. Blooming in the woods until very late in the autumn, the flowers are small, light blue, and rarely white.

The tiny yellow flowers of the New England aster are ringed by large, pink bracts

Wavy-leaved aster, *Aster undulatus*
This is another, blue, small-flowered plant common in the woods. Its stem is rough. The leaves are heart-shaped with winged petioles clasping the stem.

Annual salt marsh aster, *Aster subulatus*
This species is found almost exclusively growing in salt marshes along the Atlantic Coast. A small plant, its leaves are long and narrow, clasping the stem. The flowers of the annual salt marsh aster are light purplish-blue and very small.

Perennial salt marsh aster, *Aster tenuifolius*

Like the preceding seaside aster, this species is a small plant with sessile linear leaves and pale purple flowers, but the flowers are much larger than those of the annual.

White-flowered Asters
Heath Aster, *Aster ericoides*
In open places everywhere this small white aster blooms from early fall until late November. The basal leaves of the heath aster are spatulate, and its many branches are covered with tiny linear leaves giving it the appearance of a small bush.

Dense-flowered aster, *Aster multiflorus*
Common in open sandy places, but less common than the heath aster, this species has erect, wiry branches thickly covered with tiny leaves and small white flowers.

Small white aster, *Aster vimineus*
This small-flowered species is much like the dense-flowered aster, but it grows in moist soil and has horizontal rather than erect branches. The branches are crowded with tiny flowers and leaves.

Starved aster, *Aster lateriflorus*
Like the small white aster, the branches of the starved aster are horizontal and are covered with tiny flowers and leaves, but the stem leaves are oval and much longer than the leaves of other small-flowered white asters.

White wood aster, *Aster divaricatus*
From August until late in the fall the white wood aster blooms in the woods, where the blue wood aster, the wavy-leaved aster, and the large-leaved aster are also found. The flowers of the white wood aster are about an inch broad and the leaves are heart-shaped, the lower ones larger than the upper ones.

Large-leaved aster, *Aster macrophyllus*
Blooming in the woods, this species often forms carpets of large, rough, heart-shaped leaves. It is similar to the white wood aster but can always be identified by the large basal leaves. The stems bear smaller, more oval leaves and bluish-white flowers rise out of the basal leaves.

Panicled white aster, *Aster paniculatus*
This aster is common in wet places along the edge of woods. It is a tall plant with dark green, narrow, pointed leaves and white flowers, slightly larger than a nickel, borne in rather loose, flat-topped clusters. —A.M.M.

ASTRONOMY (*See under Season; Star*)

ATTWATER PRAIRIE CHICKEN (*See under Prairie Chicken*)

AUDUBON
John James Audubon, for whom the Audubon Society was named (*see National Audubon Society*), great painter of American birds, was born April 26, 1785 at Les Cayes, in what is now the Republic of Haiti. His father, Jean Audubon, was a French merchant marine captain; his mother a Mademoiselle Rabin of Les Cayes. Audubon himself said that he had been born of a Creole mother in New Orleans; but until documentary evidence was brought to light by Francis Hobart Herrick, a 20th-century American biographer, the exact date and place were uncertain, and gave rise to romantic speculation about Audubon's parentage. It is still sometimes suggested that the artist was actually the lost Dauphin of France, although there are no facts to support the theory.
During the American Revolution

John James Audubon, a self-portrait

Capt. Jean Audubon had been taken prisoner by the British in New York, and after his release he saw the surrender of Cornwallis at Yorktown in 1781. He had already been engaged in the sugar and coffee trade with the West Indies, and following the Revolution spent much of his time there as a merchant, planter, and slave trader. On a trip to his home in France in 1789 he took with him the four-year-old boy who was then known as Fougere Rabin, or Jean Rabin Fougere.

Captain Audubon and his wife had no children of their own, and in 1794 they legally adopted the boy. A few years later, at the insistence of Madame Audubon, he was baptized Jean Jacques Fougere Audubon. His boyhood was spent in the city of Nantes and at his father's country villa in nearby Coueron, on the Loire. He readily acquired the gentlemanly arts of hunting, fencing, dancing, and playing the violin; but he had little interest in going to school, preferring instead to roam through the countryside. He later wrote that during these years he made some 200 drawings of birds. For some months in 1802-03 he was a pupil in the studios of the court painter Jacques Louis David. Then, late in 1803, at the age of 18, he set out for the New World.

Captain Audubon evidently intended his son for the French navy; but to give him a taste of the world and some experience in business management, decided to send the youth to care for Mill Grove Farm, a property near Philadelphia purchased by the captain during one of his sojourns in the United States. Immediately after his arrival in New York, young Audubon contracted yellow fever, and it was not until he had been nursed back to health in a Quaker household at Morristown, New Jersey, that he saw Mill Grove for the first time. By now he was quite a handsome youth, a graceful dancer and skater, and something of a dandy when he chose to be; but roving through the woods about Mill Grove was more to his taste than polite society. Because he knew little English he was in no hurry to seek out the British family who were his nearest neighbors. When he finally did so, he was received by the eldest daughter, Lucy Green Bakewell, who was then barely 16. Before the year was out she had agreed to marry him, and early in 1805 Audubon was on his way back to France to ask his father's approval of the match.

Jean had other worries concerning one Francis Dacosta, who had acquired a half interest in Mill Grove and with whom he had been continually at odds. He spent a year in France, mainly at the country house in Coueron, where he made many new drawings. In the spring of 1806, having apparently won his point with Captain Audubon, he sailed for New York in the company of Ferdinand Rozier, with whom he planned to set up a business partnership. This time his stay at Mill Grove was brief; by September the remainder of the interest in that property had been acquired by Dacosta, and Audubon spent the next year working in a New York commission house operated by Lucy's uncle, Benjamin Bakewell. In the fall of 1807, Audubon made a trip with Rozier to Louisville, where they had decided to open a frontier store.

On April 5, 1808, Audubon and Lucy Bakewell were married, and they spent their honeymoon traveling overland and down the Ohio to Louisville. There, in June 1809, their son Victor Gifford was born; and there, in March 1810, Audubon had a visit from a melancholy stranger by the name of Alexander Wilson, later to be known as the "Father of American Ornithology," who carried a portfolio under his arm. Wilson had conceived the idea of painting all the birds of North America and had made the trip in search of new birds and also of subscribers to the work he hoped to publish.

Neither of these extraordinary men

had ever heard of the other, nor could they have had an inkling of the controversy that was later to rage around them and their work; one that has not quite subsided even now. Just what happened during that meeting is not clear; Audubon's own account of it was written years afterward, and Wilson's journal did not refer to it directly. But 10 years later Audubon was devoting himself to the same project.

Long before that, his ramblings through the woods in search of birds, which he had continued to draw and paint, were interfering with his ability to make a living. That he had no talent for business was already clear. Moving the business with Rozier from Louisville down the river to Henderson, Kentucky, did not improve matters, nor did a further move, in 1811, to the frontier post of Sainte-Genevieve in what is now Missouri. Here the partnership with Rozier came to an end, and Audubon returned to Henderson on foot.

There, one venture after another ended in failure, and in 1819 Audubon was jailed at Louisville for debt. He went bankrupt, and was left with nothing but his clothes, his gun, and his drawings of birds. In an attempt to earn a living he did crayon portraits and worked briefly as a taxidermist at a museum in Cincinnati. There he brought his family, which now included a second son, John Woodhouse Audubon.

It was at this time that Audubon resolved to publish an ornithology of North America. He had the gallant encouragement of his wife, who now showed the steadiness and resourcefulness needed to help while Audubon began his life's work. She found work as a teacher and governess, first in Cincinnati, later in New Orleans and Natchez and at Saint Francisville in Louisiana,

Belted kingfishers

Roseate spoonbill

Brown pelican

Snowy owls

Mallard ducks

Canvasbacks

Summer tanagers

Wild turkey

Long-billed curlews

Audubon reproductions from the original Elephant Folio

to support herself and her family during her husband's six-year odyssey from town to town and from wilderness to wilderness, collecting, observing, and painting birds.

During much of this time Audubon was accompanied by the youthful Joseph Mason, who joined Audubon's first expedition down the Ohio and the Mississippi to New Orleans, and who contributed botanical details to many of the paintings. Almost invariably, each new return from the wilderness to civilization found Audubon penniless, unkempt, and hungry. To maintain himself he continued painting his portraits of wealthy clients; occasionally he gave lessons in French, dancing, or even swimming, as well as drawing, and for a few months he tutored a young girl, Eliza Pirrie, at Oakley Plantation near Saint Francisville, where he did some of his finest paintings.

A year later, Lucy Audubon opened a private school at Beechwoods, a nearby plantation, where she remained for the next five years, and where her husband visited briefly between his field excursions. On some journeys he had the company of John Stein, an artist who gave him his first lessons in oil painting. Another companion was his son Victor, who late in 1823 traveled with him as far as Louisville. Here Victor became a clerk to an uncle, Nicholas Berthoud. Again Audubon maintained himself by painting not only portraits but riverboat panels and even street signs; but he had made up his mind to go to Philadelphia in search of a publisher or patron. In 1824 he traveled there, but the business trip was not a success.

Alexander Wilson's ornithology had been published, and Wilson himself had been dead since 1813; but Wilson's friend and promoter George Ord was still alive and extremely partisan. Perhaps it was not surprising that a newcomer who set out to surpass Wilson, the "Father of American Ornithology," should have been looked upon as an upstart. Nevertheless, during Audubon's stay in Philadelphia he earned the friendship of Edward Harris and Charles Lucien Bonaparte. The painter Thomas Sully was sufficiently impressed with his work to give him letters of introduction to other artists in New York. There he was kindly received and became a member of the Lyceum of Natural History. But the problem of being without publisher or patron remained. It was apparently during an expedition to Lake Ontario and Lake Champlain, in search of birds, that he came to the conclusion that he must look for a publisher abroad.

The immediate problem was one of finances, and his first step was to go to Louisiana once more. At Pittsburgh, on the way, he met the painter George Lehman, who later became one of his assistants. By the end of November Jean was back with Lucy at Saint Francisville, where for the next 18 months he gave lessons in French, music, drawing, and dancing.

On May 17, 1826, he sailed from New Orleans, arriving in England on July 21. After an exhibition of his paintings at the Royal Institution he found himself hailed as the "American Genius." He promptly launched a subscription campaign for the work he hoped to publish, and by the end of October an Edinburgh engraver and painter, W. H. Lizars, was already at work on the plates.

Audubon shortly became the newest social idol; honors came to him from all sides. The project for which he had come went less smoothly. There were difficulties with Lizars, and after the first few plates the work was transferred to Robert Havell, Jr., in London. Although in the end Audubon left increasing responsibility to the engraver, at the beginning he closely supervised each operation. Because he was determined to depict each bird in its natural size, double elephant folio plates (measuring approximately 29½ by 29½ inch-

American flamingo from Audubon's Elephant Folio

es untrimmed) were to be used. The rendering of minute variations of texture in the originals called for a combination of engraving on copper with aquatint; and after it was printed, each plate had to be colored by hand. So massive and exacting a project was costly. Honors and social success were one thing, but finding subscribers to a work to be issued in parts, and priced at $1,000 a set, was another.

A relentless campaign for subscribers eventually took Audubon to France,

Prairie chickens

where he was acclaimed by the eminent zoologist Georges Cuvier. When he returned to America, he had been away almost three years. Such was the pressure of the work still to be done that he spent the summer in the east, drawing new species of birds. It was not until October that he finally arrived at Saint Francisville and saw his wife again.

The next year Audubon returned to England, and this time Lucy went with him. On their way to New York they stopped in Washington and met the President, Andrew Jackson. The years between 1830 and 1838 were unceasingly active. For Audubon himself there were two return trips to the United States in search of birds not yet painted —in Florida, Maine, New Brunswick, Labrador, and Texas — and meetings

Ivory-billed woodpeckers

with a growing circle of assistants and collaborators.

That the man who had shown no talent for business now showed an ability to command and coordinate so many loyalties was perhaps partly the result of his own single-minded devotion to the project. The inner circle consisted of his two sons: he took John Woodhouse with him to Labrador, he sent Victor to England to take charge of the publication. George Lehman went with him to Florida; at Charleston Audubon

Baltimore orioles

was assisted by a young lady named Maria Martin.

Abroad, he had enlisted the services of a young Scottish naturalist, William McGillivray, who by the end of 1830 was already at work on a text to accompany *The Birds of America,* to be known as the *Ornithological Biography.* McGillivray's main assignment was to write technical descriptions from bird specimens forwarded to him by the artist; the rest of the work was almost entirely in Audubon's own words.

Edward Harris interceded in a squabble over permission to use the specimens in the Townsend-Nuttall collection at the Philadelphia Academy of Natural Sciences. The collection included many western species Audubon had never seen, and Harris went with Audubon on a bird-collecting expedition to Texas, for which the United States Government gave financial aid. But one of Audubon's most fruitful collaborations was with the Reverend John Bachman, who during the winter of 1833-34 and again in 1836-37 opened his Charleston household to the entire Audubon family. In the spring of 1837 John Woodhouse Audubon married Bachman's daughter Maria Rebecca; two years later Victor married her sister Eliza.

Passenger pigeons

Meanwhile, in 1838, the volumes of *The Birds of America,* begun nine years before, had been completely published. The finished work of four volumes contained a total of 435 plates showing 1,065 birds of 489 different species. In all, fewer than 200 sets had been printed. Audubon and his family celebrated the occasion by going with Audubon's friend William McGillivray on a tour of Scotland. But the artist and his Scottish collaborator were soon back in Edinburgh and at work once again on the *Ornithological Biography.* In 1839, after the fifth and last volume of the *Ornithological Biography* had been published, Audubon returned to America, this time to stay.

During the next few years a seven-volume octavo edition of *The Birds of America* was published, illustrated with lithographs. Another event for Audubon was his purchase of a plot overlooking the Hudson, in what is now the Washington Heights section of Manhattan, where Audubon and his sons built houses of their own. They called the place "Minnie's Land," from "Minnie," a pet name of Audubon for his wife Lucy.

With John Bachman of Charleston, South Carolina, and a new circle of collaborators and assistants, Audubon began a second major work, *The Viviparous Quadrupeds of North America.* In search of mammal specimens and a renewed taste of the wilderness, Audubon set out in March 1843 with his friend and financial supporter, Edward Harris; the painter Isaac Sprague; and two other assistants, on what was to be his last expedition—a trip up the Missouri River that took them as far as the Yellowstone. Audubon was then fifty-eight years old. An observer who met him during the return trip saw him as a picturesque old man with flowing white hair and beard, but still hawk-like, keen-eyed, and vigorous. By 1847 a decline in Audubon's health had set in, and year by year what remained of his old animation ebbed away. The paintings for *The Viviparous Quadrupeds of North America,* some of which had been done by the elder Audubon, others by his son John Woodhouse, had been completed, and the three folio volumes of lithographs were published between 1845 and 1848. The three volumes of text, edited by John Bachman, were not completed until after Audubon's death. On January 27, 1851, in his 66th year, Audubon died at his home overlooking the Hudson River in New York.

Lucy Audubon outlived her husband by more than two decades. To support herself after he died she again took up teaching, and eventually sold the originals of *The Birds of America* to the New York Historical Society, which still has possession of them and sometimes exhibits them. In later years one of Lucy Audubon's former pupils, George Bird Grinnell, editor of *Forest and Stream,* had a vivid memory of the paintings as they hung in her house at "Minnie's Land," and of what she had told him of Audubon himself. When concern over the wanton destruction of wild birds led George Bird Grinnell to form a society on their behalf, he named it for Audubon. Thus, in 1886, the movement that still bears the artist's name was born. —Ay. C.

Audubon the Artist

What is the quality which distinguishes any great artist from his colleagues? Why, for example, do the paintings of John James Audubon dominate the art of bird painting although there have been a score of other highly successful painters in this field?

The answer lies largely in Audubon's ability to infuse his work with vitality and enthusiasm. Audubon excelled as an artist because he had a deep understanding and passion for nature, because he drew birds and other animals, flowers and trees with intense concentration and with amazing fidelity, while yet conveying the spirit of a subject in an often arresting and original composition.

Oddly enough, Audubon has been placed first among artists of western culture as a painter of birds on the basis of reproductions which, though skillfully done for their time, bear only superficial resemblance to the greatly superior originals. Audubon's stature as an artist should rest on his original works, not on reproductions.

Robert Havell, the English engraver, watered down Audubon's work, both literally and figuratively, because he colored the engravings only with watercolor. Audubon combined pencil, watercolor, pastel, crayon, ink, oil and lacquer in a variety of inventive and original combinations to imitate as accurately as possible the texture and color of feathers and fur, flowers, and trees.

No artist before or after him has conveyed texture with more accuracy; few artists have had as finely developed a sense of color. Not many artists have painted the bark of a dead tree with more vigor and texture, blossoms with greater delicacy, leaves with more waxy sheen. His ability to paint a blade of grass with a few strokes of the brush recalls the brush drawings of great early Chinese artists – to which Audubon's work has been compared.

But, whereas the Chinese animal and floral paintings are reserved and poetical, Audubon's work is boldly dramatic, has more depth, is fresh and direct rather than studied and formalized. Audubon's birds are often portrayed in violent or gentle motion, but his greatest gift was to portray latent life in a perched bird or a sitting rabbit or squirrel.

Audubon's fame rests firmly on his drawings and paintings of birds, as it should, since they were the central interest in his life. Even after completing *Birds of America,* he continued to draw birds for the smaller edition that followed. Next in importance are his watercolors of the smaller mammals or quadrupeds, as they were then called, the majority done between 1841 and 1845. Often well composed, always skillfully drawn, they consist generally of an animal or a group of animals without background.

Audubon also made accurate oil painting copies of his watercolors. He freely and quickly painted oils of birds and mammals, such as the "Eagle Seizing a Highland Lamb," "English Pheasants Surprised by Spanish Dog," and "Two Cats Fighting Over a Dead Squirrel." His favorite, most frequently repeated, subject was the "Entrapped Otter." Most of these Audubon painted in Great Britain between 1826 and 1829.

His chalk or pencil portraits, primarily drawn in Louisville, Cincinnati, and New Orleans between 1819 and 1826, though executed only to help support himself and his family, are often strong drawings, full of vitality and character. The early ones are stiff profiles, the later portraits were done with swift skill. They are, however, among the finest portrait drawings of their time and place. But the six or more oil portraits of about 1823 that definitely can be ascribed to Audubon show a hesitance and clumsiness in a medium he felt he never mastered.

The rest of his work consists of three large landscapes in oil, only one of which has been located; his watercolors of bird eggs which, because of space limitations, he did not reproduce in *Birds of America;* a unique painting of a dog and dead birds in the foreground with a man in the distance hunting ducks; and numerous landscape sketches, most of which may no longer exist. They are possibly no major artistic loss, since the landscapes he drew as background for his birds bear out his rather low opinion of them. Across the sky of one he wrote the following instruction to Havell, "Amend this Rascally Sky and Water."

It is difficult to estimate how many works Audubon produced, partly because, in his expansive enthusiasm, the artist was inclined to exaggerate. It seems reasonable to assume that he made at least 1,000 pictures of birds, most of which contain more than two individuals; 78 watercolors of mammals, possibly 100 portraits, and as many landscape sketches and watercolors of eggs.

More amazing, however, than his output was Audubon's development as an artist. His early drawings reveal that his talent was not precocious. He excelled because, never satisfied, he drew the same birds and plants over and over. Artists such as Audubon, who must work hard to produce work acceptable to their own high critical standards, often surpass artists of greater facility but less energy and less desire for excellence. —E.H.D.

Audubon's Animals

Although Audubon's chief fame is due to his paintings of birds, these were not his only subjects. Even while working on *The Birds of America,* hc painted about 50 insects, showing most of them as victims of some feathered predator. Some insects are too conventionalized to be recognizable, but others are quite accurate portraits, and the species can be identified. Among these are a tiger swallowtail, a buckeye butterfly, the luna, Io, and cecropia moth, the caterpiller of a monarch butterfly, a measuring worm, and even a black widow spider.

A companion series to *The Birds of America* is the *Viviparous Quadrupeds of North America,* a three-volume series completed after Audubon's death. Work began on the project after the wonderful reception of *The Birds of America,* and it was obvious from the start that

Audubon intended that it would be just as complete, as artistic, and as worthy as his first great effort. Furthermore, he had his two sons to help him. Both John Woodhouse Audubon and Victor Gifford Audubon were competent artists in their own rights; they collaborated on all the paintings in Volume III and much of the work in Volume II. The 155 plates in these three volumes compare favorably with Audubon's best work in *The Birds of America.* —G.B.S.

Northern hares

Ocelot, or leopard cat

Swift fox

Long-haired squirrels

Nine-banded armadillo

Pronghorn, or antelope

Grey fox

AUDUBON MEDAL

In May 1946, at a meeting of the Board of Directors of the National Audubon Society, it was proposed that the National Audubon Society originate a medal for distinguished, individual service to conservation. The medal was to be awarded, from time to time, to persons whom the Board felt had accomplished outstanding work in conservation.

At a meeting in September 1946, the Board agreed upon these principles, and subsequently engaged the noted sculptor, Paul Manship, to design the medal.

The bronze medal, up to 1963, had been awarded to the following; in 1947 to Hugh H. Bennett, at that time Chief of the Soil Conservation Service; in 1949 to Ira N. Gabrielson, President of the Wildlife Management Institute, formerly Director, United States Fish and Wildlife Service; in 1950 to John D. Rockefeller, Jr., for his great contributions to the national parks; in 1952 to Louis Bromfield for his leadership in conservation farming, writing, and lecturing; in 1955 to Walt Disney for his major part in creating a world-wide appreciation and understanding of nature; in 1956 to Ludlow Griscom for his contributions to wildlife conservation and to the work of the National Audubon Society; in 1959 to Olaus J. Murie, largely for his lifetime of work as a leading champion of wilderness preservation; in 1960 to Jay N. Darling for his forceful crusading work against waste and despoiling of natural resources; in 1961 to Clarence N. Cottam in recognition of his distinguished career as a scientist, educator, and administrator in wildlife conservation and management; in 1962 to Justice William O. Douglas, "eloquent and militant spokesman for conservation;" and in 1963 to Rachel Carson, author of *Silent Spring*, a book that alerted and aroused the public to the dangers of needless chemical pollution of our environment.—J.K.T.

AUDUBON SOCIETY *(See under National Audubon Society)*

AUK

Auks are members of a family of birds (Alcidae) of the polar seas, occupying the same ecological niche in the Arctic waters as penguins do in the Antarctic. The plumage is predominantly black and white, and some species have colorful bill structures. All the auks feed upon fishes and other marine life obtained by swimming under water. Puffins, guillemots, the razorbill, extinct great auk, murres, and auklets are all in the auk family. —G.B.S.

AUKLET

Crested Auklet

Other Common Names—Sea quail
Scientific Name—*Aethia cristatella*
Family—Alcidae (auks, murres, and puffins)
Order—Charadriiformes
Size—Length, 9½ inches
Range—Western Alaska and northeastern Asia

The crested auklet is one of twelve stubby, short-winged seabirds of the northern Pacific waters. All of them feed on small forms of marine life, obtained at the surface or, by diving, from beneath it. The crested auklet is a dull, slaty gray, somewhat lighter on the under surface. The adult has a thin white plume, drooping down and back from the corner of each eye.

In spring and summer the rather thick bill in this species turns a bright orange. The crest lengthens and curves forward until it nearly touches the bill. In the winter, this adornment is lost.

Small though it is, the crested auklet has a loud cry when on its nesting grounds, a honking, grunting sound.

Similar seabirds in the northern Pacific and Bering Sea are the four murrelets, two puffins, and five other auklets. The only small seabird of this size in the northern Atlantic is the dovekie.

—G.B.S.

AVIAN BOTULISM (*See under Botulism*)

AVOCET

American Avocet

Other Common Names—Blue shanks, blue stocking, Irish snipe

Scientific Name—*Recurvirostra americana*

Family—Recurvirostridae (avocets and stilts)

Order—Charadriiformes

Size—Length, 16 to 18 inches

Range—Breeds from eastern Washington and southern Saskatchewan to southern California, Texas, and eastward to the upper Mississippi Valley. Winters from the Gulf Coast to California and south to Central America

The avocet stands out as the most showy of all the North American shorebirds. Its white body and black, white-striped wings, make it conspicuous at a great distance. The head and neck are tinged pink in the breeding season.

The wingspread of the American avocet (from tip to tip of its wings) is 20 inches. The long, upward-curving bill is extremely unusual among birds. The partially webbed blue feet—the avocet is often called blue shanks—enable it to swim with ease when in the water searching for food.

American avocets nest in colonies in marshes or at the muddy edges of ponds and lakes. The nest is merely a slight depression in the marsh, lined with

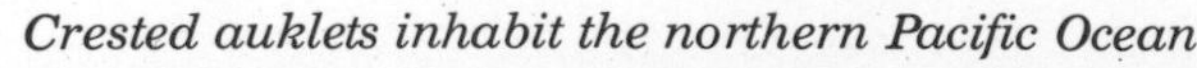

Crested auklets inhabit the northern Pacific Ocean

grass, where four, spotted and blotched eggs are laid. If threatened with flooding, avocets have been known to add several inches of material to the nest to raise it to a safe level. In common with other waders, the newly-hatched avocets are precocial and can run about and pick up food very shortly after they are hatched.

The avocet gets its living in or about the water. It eats small snails and water insects, both in their adult and larval stages. On salt marshes it collects worms from the muddy water through which it wades. It uses a variety of techniques to acquire its food—it runs after insects, swims from one shallow to another.

American avocets are common in suitable places in the far-western states, but early in the 19th century they were also abundant along the Atlantic Coast. Naturalists found them breeding in the salt marshes of New Jersey. Their almost total disappearance from the eastern United States was attributed to hunters. In examining the published lists of birds for the various states east of the Mississippi River, it is not unusual today to find the avocet listed as a "rare transient" or an "occasional visitor." The lack of hunting pressure, now that the shorebirds are protected by law, may some day restore the American avocet as part of the wildlife of eastern marshes. —A.B. Jr.

The American avocet lives in marshes or along the edges of ponds and lakes

B

BACTERIA

These are microscopic plants (classified by scientists as being between plants and animals) that do not contain chlorophyll, have a simple nucleus, lack specialized structures (except for flagellae in some forms), and are placed in the class Schizomycetes. They are referred to as bacteria, from a Greek word meaning a small staff. They are larger than the viruses, which can pass through filters that do not permit the passage of bacteria.

A diverse group, bacteria may not be all of the same origin. Shape is variable; some are rod-shaped, others round, some spiral, and some link together in long strands. With all but a few, reproduction is by simple fission. Most forms have a rigid cell wall. A few have flagellae, thin whiplike strands of tissue that are used for locomotion.

Bacteria require a moist environment, and are usually found in water or other fluids. Some species have the faculty of encysting, of enclosing the living tissue in a wall of resistant material that prevents desiccation.

Bacteria are of great and direct importance to man. They materially assist in the making of cheese, vinegar, antibiotics, vitamins, and in such processes as the retting (soaking and loosening of fiber) of vegetable fibers and in sewage treatment plants. Other bacteria are the causative agents in such diseases as brucellosis, cholera, diphtheria, dysentery, gonorrhoea, meningitis, plague, pneumonia, scarlet fever, and a number of other human ills.

In the plant world, nitrogen-fixing bacteria in the roots of leguminous plants allow the plants to use this valuable chemical element. On the negative side, they cause blights, wilts, galls, tumors, and rots. —G.B.S.

BADGER

Other Common Names—None
Scientific Name—*Taxidea taxus*
Family—Mustelidae (weasels, skunks, and allies)
Order—Carnivora
Size—Body length, 11 to 22 inches; tail, 4 to 6 inches; weight, 13 to 25 pounds
Range—Western North America, from southern Canada to northern Mexico, east to central Texas, Kansas, and northwestern Ohio. Absent from western Washington and Oregon

The earthbound badger is a clumsy animal, unable to climb trees, to swim, or to run very fast. It is especially adapted, through evolution, for digging.

It has a stocky body, long, shaggy hair, short legs and tail, strong claws, a short neck, and sharp teeth. Its ears are short and rounded, and its head flattened. Ambling along on the ground, the badger's body sprawls out in a seemingly unsupported manner.

Ground squirrels are one of its chief sources of food, yet a ground squirrel can easily outdistance a badger. Once the squirrel seeks refuge in its underground den, however, the badger digs a shaft straight down over its unsuspecting quarry, never failing to hit the exact spot where its prey is hiding.

With its trundling gait, the badger can easily be overtaken by a dog or a coyote, but a cornered badger can escape by digging swiftly into the ground. Its powerful legs and long claws shower the soil in all directions and in a few minutes only a plugged burrow marks its departure.

Because of its ferocity when cornered, few animals attack it. When approached unexpectedly it will lie flat, hoping to be unobserved. If a person should come close to it, it will start to dig wildly, but if unable to take cover soon enough, it will turn to fight and may snap at one's ankles. It has a tenacious grip.

The flat, open country where the badger lives offers little cover except what it provides for itself. It seems to prefer the desert and arid plains where it is easier for it to dig into the soil and disappear to escape its enemy.

Little is known about the mating habits of the badger, but it probably mates in the autumn or winter. In spring the female has one litter, usually in May or June, with one to five young. The eyes of the young open when they are four to six weeks old. The underground home is at the end of a 6 to 30 foot tunnel.

The badger usually hunts alone and at night, although it may be seen in daytime at the entrance to its den. It feeds on rats, squirrels, mice, rabbits, insects, snakes, snails, and, sometimes, groundnesting birds and their eggs. It may sometimes be seen along the edges of dunes at night where it hunts for lizards.

The badger is helpful to the farmer in keeping rodents under control. On the other hand, the open burrows and piles of earth are at times hazardous to horsemen—ranchers and cowboys.

In colder areas the badger sleeps through the winter, occasionally rousing itself to hunt for a midwinter snack, but in the warmer regions it is active all year.

The upper parts of the badger are a grayish color, with a white stripe extending from the nose to the shoulders. The throat is white, the underparts a buff color, the feet dark brown or black.

The badger belongs to a family of weasel-like animals—the skunks, minks, weasels, otters, fishers, and wolverines.

The badger is an expert excavator and can disappear into the ground in minutes

The soft rock formations of Badlands National Monument have been severely eroded

BADLANDS NATIONAL MONUMENT
Location—Southern South Dakota
Size—207 square miles
Mammals—Deer, squirrels, chipmunks, prairie dogs, badgers, hares, rabbits, foxes, bobcats
Birdlife—Rock wrens, Say's Phoebes, mountain bluebirds, horned larks, western meadow larks, lark sparrows
Plants—Ground phlox, pasque flowers, wallflowers, evening primroses, red mallows, and other wild flowers

Clay and sandstone, eroded by water, wind, and frost, have carved a multicolored land of jagged peaks and buttes, given the name of badlands because they have no economic use. The region was once a swampy plain, and fossils are commonly found after rains.

Accommodations—Cabins are available at Cedar Pass, South Dakota
Headquarters—Cedar Pass, South Dakota

BALANCE OF NATURE

Observers of wildlife have noted that within any given territory the total number of organisms tends to remain the same over the years so long as there is no major change in the area itself.

Most plants and animals reproduce far beyond the need for replacement. In each generation, therefore, many individuals, whether weasel cubs, pine seeds, or mosquito larvae, are surplus population; they will not be needed to carry on the species. Some will find living space, food, and shelter, and live a normal life span without reproducing. Others, less fortunate, will be cropped by predators or eliminated by disease, starvation, or exposure.

This relationship between a species and its habitat is an unsteady and fluctuating balance. If one species decreases, another will fill the vacuum. It is this *tendency* to maintain a dynamic equilibrium that biologists call the "balance of nature." –G.B.S.

BARNACLE

Acorn Barnacle
Other Common Names—Rock barnacle
Scientific Name—*Balanus balanoides*
Family—Balanidae (acorn barnacles)
Order—Thoracica
Size—Height, one-quarter to two inches; diameter, less than one-half inch
Range—Worldwide in distribution

Goose Barnacle
Other Common Names—Gooseneck
Scientific Name—*Lepas fascicularis*
Family—Lepadidae (gooseneck barnacles)
Order—Thoracica
Size—Length, about two inches
Range—Worldwide in distribution

Barnacles belong to the phylum Arthropoda and the class Crustacea, along with the shrimps and the crabs. Most species of this phylum—that includes the spiders, crabs, and insects—are highly active. They move about on several pairs of legs and, as with the insects, often on wings. Young barnacles, along with the adults, have antennae, body segments, and legs. Contrasted with the immobile adults, they are active swimmers in the plankton, the community of plants and animals of microscopic and near-microscopic size that drift with the surface waters of the seas (*See Plankton*).

But the maturing barnacle, after reaching a certain size, settles down to a fixed existence. The acorn barnacle (*Balanus*) attaches its head to a rock or other solid object, casts off its shrimp-like shell, and secretes a limy covering of five plates. The feet become appendages for catching tiny marine creatures and conveying them to the mouth. The goose barnacle (*Lepas*) converts the head into a long stalk of tissue and manufactures a series of shell-like plates that resemble the body of a goose. Another member of the class (*Sacculina*) becomes a parasite on crabs and loses all specialized structures, such as legs, digestive organs, and sensory organs, and becomes a mass of undifferentiated tissue. (*See also under Crustacean*)
–G.B.S.

Yellow bass

White bass

BASS

This is the common name for many species of marine and fresh water fishes of North America. Four of the better-known are the striped bass, white bass, white perch, and yellow bass, all of which belong to the same family. All have two dorsal fins; the front fin has spiny rays that form a serrated edge. They are fine game fish, seasonally protected by laws. The largemouth bass and smallmouth bass are not classified in the bass family, but are related to the sunfishes (*See also under Fish; Sunfish*).

Striped bass

Striped Bass
Other Common Names—Rockfish, rock, striper, linesides
Scientific Name—*Roccus saxatilis*
Family—Serranidae (sea basses)
Order—Perciformes
Size—Length, to 2 feet; weight, 10 pounds
Range—In both the salt an fresh waters of the east coast of North America from the Gulf of St. Lawrence to Florida

The striped bass has a stout body that is three and one half to four times as long as it is deep. The head is long and the back slightly arched; its two dorsal fins are about equal in length. The front fin is triangular in shape while the rear fin slopes downward gradually from front to back.

The fish is silvery, olive-green in color, often with a brassy tinge. The sides are paler than the back, lined with seven or eight dark horizontal stripes, from which its name is derived. One of these stripes runs along the lateral line organ, an important sensory organ of many fishes.

Striped bass live in the ocean but spawn in either the brackish waters of river mouths or in fresh water streams inland. They have voracious appetites and feed on large numbers of smaller fishes and many kinds of small invertebrate animals.

White Bass
Other Common Names—Silver bass, silver fish, streaker
Scientific Name—*Roccus chrysops*
Family—Serranidae (sea basses)
Order—Perciformes
Size—Length, 7½ to 16 inches; weight, 2 pounds
Range—Fresh waters in and near the Great Lakes and the Mississippi and Missouri rivers

The white bass resembles the average-sized, or smaller, striped bass, but its back is more sharply arched and its lower jaw protrudes slightly in front of its upper jaw. In addition, its tongue is equipped with small teeth. The stripes that run along its sides are not as pronounced as those of the striped bass. Its two dorsal fins are located, and shaped, much like those of the striped bass and its body color is similar. Its anal fin has ten or more rays, a characteristic by which it can be distinguished from the white perch.

The white bass feeds primarily on small fishes, but it also feeds on insects and crustaceans.

Yellow Bass
Other Common Names—Streaker, black-striped bass, gold bass
Scientific Name—*Roccus mississippiensis*
Family—Serranidae (sea basses)
Order—Perciformes
Size—Length, 8 to 11 inches; weight, 1 to 2 pounds
Range—In large rivers from southern Minnesota, Wisconsin, and Indiana, south to the Tennessee River drainage in Alabama, eastern Texas, and eastern Oklahoma

The shape of the body and fins is similar to that of the other bass. Its back is dark olive-green; its sides, silvery to bright golden yellow; its belly, white. It has six or seven dusky but prominent horizontal stripes on each side. Three of the stripes on each side are above the fish's lateral line. The stripes below the lateral line are there broken or interrupted toward the tail fins.

White Perch
Scientific Name—*Roccus americanus*
Other Common Names—None
Family—Serranidae
Order—Perciformes
Size—7 to 12 inches long; weight, 1 to 2 pounds
Range—Fresh waters of eastern North America from New Brunswick, Prince Edward Island, and Nova Scotia to South Carolina

The white perch is often confused with the white bass. Although they look very much alike they can be distinguished from each other quite easily. The white perch usually has 8 or 9 (rarely 10) rays in its anal fin whereas the white bass has a minimum of 10 rays in its anal fin. Its back is a dull olivegreen with silvery reflections. The scales on the back are sometimes darker at their edges than their centers. This makes the white perch appear mottled, or to have light, wavy rows of color. The sides are lighter and more silvery than the back. Its dorsal, tail, and anal fins are silver-colored at their roots and become darker at the edges of the fins.

The white perch has been introduced into Lake Erie, the basin of Lake Ontario, and a great number of bodies of water throughout New England, New York State, and Quebec. —M.R.

BASSWOOD
Other Common Names—American linden
Scientific Name—*Tilia americana*
Range—New Brunswick, southern Quebec, Ontario, southeastern Manitoba, Maine to North Dakota, south to Maryland, Kentucky, Arkansas, Texas and eastern Kansas
Habitat—Grows best in deep, moist soils
Leaves—Four to six inches long, broadly heart-shaped, with a pointed tip and

Basswood

coarse teeth. The base is often asymmetrical. Winter buds are red
Bark—Smooth gray when young, developing dark, lengthwise furrows with some cross-cracking
Flowers—Groups, of cream-yellow blossoms, each one-half inch across, hanging on a stem from the center of a four-inch straplike bract. Very attractive to bees
Fruit—The fruit is hard, round, pealike, olive-gray, and hangs beneath the leaf

About 15 species of basswood occur in the United States, with an equal number in Europe and other parts of the world. The North American forms are all very similar. *Tilia americana* is one of the most common and most widely distributed. In Europe the common name for this tree is linden; this name is also used for much of the introduced stock that has been planted in parks and along streets in the United States.

Open-grown basswoods, or lindens, usually form a broad, rounded shape with arching branches that make a natural shaded arbor, clear of undergrowth and well-suited for benches or picnicking. The fragrant blossoms, which are attractive to bees, are a source of an excellent grade of honey.

In forests of the eastern United States, particularly on the western side of the Appalachians, American basswood is an abundant tree, much used for pulpwood, boxes, veneer, and woodenware. The pale or white wood is light and rather soft, but durable. These forest-grown trees have a tall, often irregular form. However, those growing on the edge of woods in poor soil are sometimes disfigured and dwarfed by fire and insects. Apparently this species suffers considerably unless it has soil and other conditions favorable to its particular needs.

The round, hard little seeds remain on the tree quite late. They may not fall until a strong autumn breeze loosens the seed bract to which the fruiting stem is attached. The leafy bract, with the aid of the wind, carries the seeds some distance from the tree. Many of the seeds are eaten by small mammals and birds.

In winter the basswood may be easily identified by its bright red buds with the two characteristic overlapping scales. (*See also under Tree*) —M.H.B.

BAT

Bats are both crepuscular animals—that is, active at dusk and early morning—and nocturnal—active at night. Occasionally some bats fly about during the day if disturbed from their daytime roosts, and the red bat may hunt on gloomy days or even in bright sunlight, especially during its migrations.

There are about 180 recognized species of North American bats [according to Hall and Kelson, *The Mammals of North America*] many of which are confined largely to tropical America. Some common ones of the United States are the leaf-nosed bats of the Southwest, the insect-eating bats of the United States in general—the little brown bat, big brown bat, red bat, pipistrelles, hoary bat, yellow bat, silver-haired bat, and others. There is also a group of free-tailed bats, including the mastiff bats of this family, which are larger than the so-called free-tailed bats. (*See under Mammal: The Order Chiroptera*) —J.K.T.

Little Brown Bat

Other Common Names—Myotis bat
Scientific Name—*Myotis lucifigus*
Family—Vespertilionidae (typical insect-eating bats)
Order—Chiroptera
Size—Length, 3½ to 4½ inches
Range—Throughout the northern United States including southern Alaska, and in Canada to the limit of tree growth. Absent in the southeastern and southwestern United States

In summer the little brown bat (*Myo-*

Bats are banded in the same way as birds to facilitate the study of their movements

tis lucifugus) comes out rather late in the evening, usually near the end of the twilight period when it is sometimes difficult to distinguish it in the darkness. Its flight is comparatively steady for a bat, yet even this species abruptly changes its course, ducks and dives, and sometimes turns complete somersaults in the air. Its rapid wingbeats, three per second, propel it at good speed for short distances. In its ability to catapult, dodge, and turn quickly in flight, the bat surpasses most birds. The little brown bat may frequently be seen on a summer evening, if the light and background are favorable, as it flies high over some watercourse or meadow, or around clearings in a woodland. Not infrequently it enters a building through an open door or window.

In alighting, the little brown bat, with its wings extended, catches with its hook-like claws on the thumbs the surface of whatever it alights upon, clasps the object with its hindfeet, folds its wings, and then hangs head downward. A bat thus pendant will rest or sleep for hours.

Bats differ markedly from other mammals as a result of their ability to fly. The digits of their forelimbs are greatly lengthened and form a support for each wing membrane—a thin, flexible, yet leathery skin that extends from the hind limbs and the sides of their bodies to the tips of their "fingers" and the front of their forearms. In contrast to the long, slender, clawless fingers, a bat's thumbs are short, rather heavy, and end in hooklike claws.

In all bats, the hind limbs are so rotated that the knees project backward instead of forward. In most bat species, their hind limbs and tails are connected by a skin membrane somewhat similar to their wing membranes. The breast bones and breast muscles used in flying are large compared to the hind limbs. The ear conch of the bat has a prominent slender, internal lobe called the *tragus*. Many species have growths of skin about the nose, which make them appear grotesque.

Their German name *fliedermaus* and the French term *chauve-souris*—both literally translated as *flying mouse*—indicate a common misconception as to the relationships of the bat to other animals. It is not closely related to any of the mice, but is related to shrews and moles.

Bats live in most of the temperate and tropical regions of the world. They do not like intense cold and are most numerous in the warmer climates. A number of the species feed almost exclusively on insects. One kind of tropical American bat eats small fishes, which it captures at the surface of the water. Another group of bats that live in South and Central America, known as the vampire bats, suck the blood of cattle, horses, and other large animals. In the warmer regions of the Old World, more especially in the East Indian region, there are many species of fruit-eating bats. These animals, generally known as fruit bats but sometimes called flying foxes, sleep in large colonies, hanging in trees during the daytime. But at night they fly about in search of fruiting trees. Some of the large fruit bats have a wing expanse of nearly five feet.

The commonest of the larger bats of the United States is the big brown bat, *Eptesicus fuscus,* or house bat. It lives throughout the United States, but is rare in Florida. From its nose to the tip of its tail it is slightly more than four inches long, and its wing expanse is about one foot. Really a tiny animal compared with a big fruit bat, it is large when compared with some of the smaller American bats. It is called the big brown bat to distinguish it from another species known as the little brown bat. Cinnamon-brown in general color tone, with the underparts somewhat paler, the wings dusky, and the face and ears touched with black, it is not conspicuously marked. Most of North America is its home, but like other bats it does not live in the arctic regions.

Bats build no nests, nor do they have dens like those of many other mammals. A dark nook or cranny in the cornice of some building or a retreat behind a shutter may be the home of the big brown bat, or it may sleep during the daytime behind a loose clapboard, a piece of building paper on the side of a barn or house, or even in back of a loose piece of bark on a dead tree. It also lives in caves where it rests while clinging to the walls and ceilings or in rock crevices.

Even though the big brown bat has no fixed home, it nevertheless has somewhat of a "homing instinct" and often returns night after night to the same roosting place. Frequently a colony of bats persists for years in the same location; then again the colony may suddenly move, vanishing apparently without cause or reason. When the cold of autumn and winter comes on, the big brown bat usually seeks a sheltered nook in a building or cave and falls into its winter sleep, or hibernation. A few brown bats migrate short distances to

Both the hoary bat (above) and the red bat (below) are migratory species

climates more favorable for them, but the bats that commonly migrate usually belong to other species that dwell in trees and shrubs.

The big brown bat feeds exclusively on insects, which it catches while on the wing by seizing them in its mouth. Often on a summer evening, sometimes in the larger cities, it may be hovering and dodging about a street light, capturing insects attracted by the glow. It snatches whatever insect of appropriate size passes its way, whether bug, moth, beetle, or fly. Its method of drinking is to scoop the water into its mouth as it skims the surface of a pond or stream.

Owls, falcons and some snakes prey on the big brown bat.

When flying, the big brown bat often utters a peculiar metallic *tick-tick-tick-tick-tick,* very rapidly repeated. Rarely it emits a shrill squeak, a note more characteristic of an animal in pain and one so high-pitched as not to be heard by all human ears.

"Blind as a bat" is a familiar expression. Although many animals have better sight than the bat, nevertheless this species is far from blind and can see fairly well. Much better developed are its senses of hearing and touch, particularly that of touch. The slightest pressure against its body causes it to squeak and flinch as if in agony. So acute is its sense of touch that experimenters, who covered bats' eyes with adhesive

Little brown bats hibernate during the winter, often in caves

Little brown bats

tape and then released them, discovered that bats perceive obstacles through this sense merely by the pressure of the atmosphere caused by their approach to the object. The rapid air vibrations of high-pitched sounds sent out by bats return to them like the high frequency vibrations that set up images on a radar screen. Thus bats are guided through the air as a ship is guided by radar through a fog.

Again, bats differ from other small mammals by producing few young. Sometimes two to four young arrive, but births are often single and in most species only once a year. The gestation period is very long considering the animal's size—from 50-60 days in the little brown myotis and up to eight or nine months in large bats. The length of the period may vary with metabolic changes, resting periods, and outside temperature variations. The young are large—the six-to-seven gram little brown myotis often produces a two-gram youngster. In bats that have several young the individual weights of the young bats are less.

The female bat gives birth to her young while hanging, head upward, supported by her thumbs. At birth, the newborn bat is caught in the interfemoral membrane of the mother, and it immediately climbs up her body to cling to the nipples. It clings tightly as it develops, and is carried by the mother even when she is flying about in her search for food. As her young grows rapidly, the mother carries an astonishing burden. As soon as the young are able to hang safely in their home loft or tree or other safe place—after only a few days in some species and about two weeks in others—the mother hunts alone. At about three weeks, the young bat learns to fly and is ready to hunt for itself.

Two young ones born in May or early

June constitute the family of the big brown bat, and only one brood is reared each year. The brown bat usually leaves her offspring hanging in some dark secluded nook of a building or cave when she goes abroad to hunt. The young develop rapidly, and within six weeks after birth they are able to fly.

The bat, although its metabolic rate is high, differs from other small mammals in that it is long-lived. Banded bats—little brown myotis, for example—have been recovered after 20 years in the wild. The bats' unusual ability to reduce their metabolic rate when resting and to speed it up with activity may in some way explain this. They can also vary their body temperatures with outside temperatures. These adaptations for conserving energy at any time of the year seem to be unique; certain other warm-blooded animals can do so only during hibernation.

All North American bats are an asset to man. They consume quantities of insects of the kinds that are injurious to crops. Moreover, the accumulation of excrement under a large and long-occupied bat roost creates quantities of fertilizer of high value for plant food.

—H.H.J. and H.H.

Big Brown Bat
Other Common Names—House bat
Scientific Name—*Eptesicus fuscus*
Family—Vesperilionidae (typical insect-eating bats)
Order—Chiroptera
Size—Length, four to five inches
Range—Throughout the United States (rarely in Florida); Central America, Mexico, southwestern and extreme southeastern Canada

This species of bat is brown—lighter in desert regions—with black membranes. It may be distinguished by its large size and color. The big brown bat is a dweller in buildings, crevices, and caves. In summer it comes out rather late in the evening, usually near the end of the twilight period when it is sometimes difficult to distinguish in the darkness.

The big brown bat lives everywhere from wilderness areas to cities, from sea level to fairly high mountains. It hibernates in caves, rock crevices, mines, buildings, behind signboards. It is the only bat in the northern United States and in Canada that commonly hibernates in houses.

—A.B. Jr.

Habits of Some North American Bats

Most species of bats that occur in the northern states and Canada migrate with the seasons, but some hibernate in caves below the frostline during the winter.

Only one species of the leaf-nosed bats—so named because they have a tall, triangular, fleshy outgrowth at the tip of the nose—ranges north into the United States and then only in the warm arid regions of the Southwest. This is the California leaf-nosed bat. It is a medium sized bat with large papery ears, connected across the forehead, and pale brown pelage.

By far the commonest bat in North America is the little brown bat, *Myotis lucifugus.* This genus is almost cosmopolitan, but there are a great many species, all small in size and uniformly brownish in color. The little brown bat is primarily a cave dweller but frequently takes up its abode in the roofs and corners of buildings during the summertime. In the fall most of these little bats retreat to an underground cavern below the frost line to hibernate; packed closely together in large colonies, they hang from the ceiling by their hindfeet.

Superficially the big brown bat, *Eptesicus fuscus,* is a large edition of the little brown bat. It is often referred to as the house bat because of its fondness for human habitation. However, the attraction is not food but a warm dry roosting place. While not quite as abundant as the little brown bat it is perhaps better known because it roosts in more accessible places and is common over much of North America.

The red bat, *Lasiarus borealis,* is a most attractive species. While nowhere very abundant, it is an early flier and is frequently seen. Unlike most species, the red bat is not gregarious and does not roost in caves but hangs up singly amid the foliage of trees. In color this little bat varies in shades of chestnut; the fur is delicately frosted with minute white tips. The red bat is unusual in that the female may have three and possibly four young. Most bats rarely have more than one or two young.

The great northern, *Lasiurus cinercus,* or hoary bat, has the distinction of being the largest of the northern bats. However, except for the larger size and brownish fur tipped with white, it resembles the red bat in general appearance and habits. Like the red bat, it is a tree dweller and migrates with the seasons. However, the hoary bat flies high and may be recognized by its pointed wing tips and erratic flight.

Differing from the red bat and the hoary bat in its social habits, the silver-haired bat, *Lasionycteris noctivagans,* seeks company and during migration associates in colonies of thousands. This is a small, sooty-brown species, with the tips of the longer hairs on the back frosted with ashy-white. Its favorite roosting place is a hollow tree, out of which the colony pours in rapid succession at dusk. The silver-haired bat seems to be subject to periodic fluctuations in numbers. At the height of abundance 10,000 have been recorded in one colony.

The *Pipistrellus hesperus,* and *P. subflavus,* are small brown species, often confused with the commoner little brown bat. But they average somewhat smaller in size and the fur is tricolor instead of bicolor as in the little brown bat. The pipistrelles live in the eastern and southwestern states and seem less opposed to light than most bats. Usually when roosting the pipistrelles hang in small clusters from the roof of well lighted caves or barns.

In the warmer states, as would be expected, there is a greater variety of bats. The yellow bat—*Dasypterus ega, D. intermedius,* and *D. floridanus*—a Central and South American species, ranges north into Texas and east to Florida. This bat, except for its yellowish-brown color, is much like the red bat and the interfemoral membrane is similarly haired. The Rafinesque, *Nycticeius humeralis,* of evening bat, is another warm climate species inhabiting the warmer eastern states and west to Arkansas and Texas. This is a dull brownish bat with naked membranes.

The rarest and most spectacular of our North American bats is the spotted bat, *Euderma maculata,* or jackass bat. This is a good-sized species about four and one-half inches in length. It has enormous ears and peculiar glandular swellings on the face. Its chocolate brown color, with large irregular white spots on the shoulder and rump, will distinguish this bat from all other North American bats. The spotted bat has been seen only in the southwestern states

The free-tailed bats—*Tadarida cynocephala, T. mexicana, T. femorosacca,* and *T. molossa*—are a diverse group that have reached a very high degree of specialization. Their flight is not only rapid but extremely erratic. Members of the group can readily be recognized by the free tail that extends beyond the interfemoral membrane and by their long narrow wings. The free-tailed bats are the commonest in tropical America but only two kinds range north to the United States. One is mouse-like in body form and occurs in the southern states. Colonies of many hundreds take up their abode in municipal bat roosts that have been erected for that purpose. The reason for maintaining suitable quarters for these bats is that they devour vast quantities of obnoxious insect pests.

By far the largest and the strongest

bat found in America north of the Rio Grande is the California mastiff bat, *Eumops perotis,* or bonnet bat. This robust free-tailed bat has large but low and broad ears, which cover the head like a bonnet. The fur is uniformly sooty brown in color. This bat is a formidable creature, measuring nearly six and one-half inches in length and with a set of strong sharp teeth that can inflict a severe wound. Fortunately the mastiff bat is nowhere very common and occurs only in the extreme southwestern states. —G.G.G.

BEAR

Contemporaries of prehistoric man, the bears are of comparatively recent Old World origin. Pictures of giant bears engraved on the walls of caves occupied by primitive people in Europe testify to the close association and struggle between man and bears for supremacy. Even today the American Indians and the Eskimos consider the bears a race of people capable of thought and understanding.

Confined largely to the colder regions of the northern hemisphere, bears en-

The brown bear lives along the coast of British Columbia and southern Alaska

Black bears are often seen in large groups in Yellowstone National Park, Wyoming

circle the entire globe. There are few south of the equator and none in Africa except in the Atlas Mountains and only one representative in South America. In the United States, north of the Rio Grande, there are polar bears, brown bears, blue bears, white bears, black bears, grizzly bears, and giant brown bears.

Big Brown Bear
Other Common Names—Alaskan brown bear, Kodiak bear
Scientific Name—*Ursus middendorffi*
Family—Ursidae (bears)
Order—Carnivora
Size—Body length, 8 feet; height at shoulders, 4 to 4½ feet; weight, to 1,500 pounds
Range—Northern coast of British Columbia and southern coast of Alaska and adjacent islands

The brown, or big brown bear of Alaska is a giant in the animal kingdom and the largest living carnivore in the world. Adult individuals measure eight feet in length and weigh three-quarters of a ton. Exceptionally big males are even larger. Its homeland is a narrow strip along the Pacific Coast region from the Alaskan Peninsula to British Columbia, and from the salt meadows, beaches, and coastal islands up to the ice fields. Salt air, however, seems essential to its existence for nowhere is it found beyond its influence.

As in other bears, the brown's eyes are small and close together and placed forward on its face, limiting its range of vision. A sense of smell is its great asset; in the air it can "read" the local news, detect lurking danger, sense approaching storms, and locate rich harvests. A creature of its enormous bulk can hardly be dependent on what it can forage in the way of a carnivorous diet.

In the spring the brown bear grazes like a cow and moves along cropping the grass while paying little heed to other forms of food. As summer approaches, it adds a variety of food to its daily menu. The brown bears' great feast, however, begins in June when the salmon enter the rivers to spawn and die. From far and near these brown bears

Bears are capable of bipedal locomotion

make their annual pilgrimage to the rivers swarming with salmon. Day after day they gorge themselves with salmon until the run is over. But their work does not finish there. They also clean the rivers of hordes of dead and decayed fishes. The Pacific salmon does not return to the sea but, its life cycle finished, must die after spawning.

The cubs are born in January and may vary from one to four in a litter. At first they are blind, helpless, and very small, weighing about one pound each. They do not open their eyes until about six weeks old and the following winter they den with their mother.

Despite its undisputed, all-powerful might, the big brown bear is mild and shy, seeking the solitude of its domain.

Black Bear
Other Common Names—Cinnamon bear, blue bear, glacier bear
Scientific Name—*Ursus americanus*
Family—Ursidae (bears)
Order—Carnivora
Size—Body length, five to six feet; height at shoulder, two to three feet; weight, 200 to 300 pounds
Range—Practically all of wooded North America, including the Mexican Plateau

Most versatile of the bears, the black bear has a number of color variations. Up around the glaciers of Alaska it is blue instead of black; on the islands of the inland passage of British Columbia it is snow-white; west of the Mississippi River it is a cinnamon bear; and in the East it is a normal black bear. It is essentially a forest dweller and versed in the art of climbing. However, it does not run up a tree like a squirrel but flings its arms and legs around the tree trunk in a loose easy motion. In descending, it backs down tail first.

Tree-climbing with the black bear is more of a stunt and prank than a necessity. It has few natural enemies and its den and most of its food are on the ground. It probably climbs to go bird-egging and to shake acorns and chestnuts out of trees.

Normally, the black bear is peaceable and retiring. Instances of its aggressiveness are considered exceptional. As much as it desires meat, it rarely kills any of the larger animals—although on occasion it will devour fieldmice, ground squirrels, chipmunks, and other forms of small animal life that live on or in the ground.

In the northern country wild berries are abundant and the black bear is content to feast on the bountiful supply while it lasts. In the spring and fall it subsists on roots of various plants, supplemented with grubs and insects. Black bears are especially fond of ant eggs. As most people know who have a cabin in the northern woodlands, the bear has

Grizzly bears
Alaskan brown bear

a preference for sweetmeats and will tear into a cabin if it contains a can of molasses or honey.

All ordinary bears in northern regions hibernate during winter. Unless mild weather temporarily rouses them, they sleep until spring.

Strangely, the baby black bears, usually twins, are born while the mother is still sealed up in her winter den. At birth they have their eyes closed and are exceedingly small, weighing at most some 10 to 12 ounces. This is about one two-hundredths of the mother's weight and is proportionately far less than any other placental mammal's young. They grow rapidly but do not reach maturity until nearly four years old. Solitary in its way of life, half a dozen black bears may be seen feeding peaceably together on one hillside where the blueberries or blackberries are especially abundant.

Though it usually likes its own company best, the black bear has a well-known method of communication. Most animals have a well-beaten road or trail along which they frequently travel and the black bear is no exception. Along the bear trails are certain trees marked with tooth and claw scratches. On approaching one of these signposts, the bear carefully examines it for several minutes and apparently gathers some information about the preceding traveler. It then rises up on its hind legs, embraces the tree, adds another mark on the bark and passes on its way. Usually the latest recordings are the highest. There is little doubt but that such a universal habit among bears must have a definite object. It is reasonable to assume that a bear with its remarkable senses of touch and smell would have little difficulty in reading these signposts and thereby determine the sex, age, and perhaps even something about the disposition of the previous traveler.

Bears are excellent swimmers and voluntarily swim across swift rivers and big lakes. They also have a habit of wallowing like pigs in the mud to rid themselves of insect pests.

Grizzly Bear
Other Common Names—None
Scientific Name—*Ursus horribilis*
Family—Ursidae (bears)
Order—Carnivora
Size—Body length, 6 to 7 feet; height at shoulder, 3 to 3½ feet; weight, 325 to 850 pounds
Range—Northwestern Canada and Alaska, Montana, and Wyoming

The grizzly bear was not so named on account of its ferocious disposition but because of its gray coat. The name also distinguishes it from the black bear in its brown color phases. The silver-tipped brown coat, humped shoulders, and the long, nearly straight claws on its forefeet are peculiarities of its particular race. It is, by reason of its giant strength and courage, the king of beasts in western North America. The terrific impact from a lightning blow by one of its huge paws is sufficient to break the neck of a mighty bison and has earned for it the respect of both man and beast.

The best authorities on wildlife, however, claim that the grizzly rarely attacks man unless provoked. Injure or molest one and it is terrible in its anger. The grizzly is well aware of its great strength and knows how to use it to the best advantage. Despite its large size and lumbering gait, it is swift in action and can travel at the rate of a good horse.

Fortunately the adult grizzly cannot climb a tree, a fact that doubtlessly saved the life of many a pioneer and lone prospector. The cubs are excellent climbers and even in the adolescent stage, up to two years, can go up a tree with surprising agility. Before the use of repeating rifles the grizzly was lord over all it surveyed. It openly took what it wanted and none dared question its right. Both the Indian and the white settlers stepped aside as it marched triumphantly along the trail. With the introduction of modern firearms the grizzly recognized defeat and has taught its children to shun the high-

The black bear is a forest dweller and feeds largely on berries, roots, and shoots

ways of civilization and seek safety in flight when the hated scent of man flows down the breeze.

The grizzly is basically a friendly creature in captivity. It will, in a playful gesture, probably break a man's arm or crush his back in with a slap but it does not mean any harm; it does not realize the frailty of the human body. Its ways of life are similar to those of the black bear except that the grizzly is more carnivorous and has a quicker temper.

Originally the grizzly roamed over most of western North America, from Minnesota to the coast and from Alaska south to central Mexico. Today it is still prevalent in western Canada and Alaska, but outside of parks only a limited few subsist south of the Canadian border. On the mountain a bounteous supply of food is found in season, for the grizzly considers almost every living thing (except poisonous plants) as food – all manner of plants, insects, reptiles, amphibians, fishes, birds, eggs, and mammals. In the early spring when it first comes out of hibernation it is a vegetarian. But before the summer is over it feasts not only on berries and nuts but also digs up badgers, gophers, ground squirrels, grubs, and insects.

One of the largest wild grizzlies ever recorded weighed 1,100 pounds; however, 500 pounds is nearer the average weight for adult males. The life-span of a grizzly may reach twenty-five years, though twenty is a ripe old age for any bear and few are physically fit to maintain themselves for a longer time.

Polar Bear
Other Common Names—Arctic bear
Scientific Name—*Thalarctos maritimus*
Family—Ursidae (bears)
Order—Carnivora
Size—Body length, 6½ to 7½ feet; height at shoulder, 3 to 4 feet; weight, 600 to 1,100 pounds
Range—Ice floes and coastal areas of the Arctic Ocean

The home of the polar bear is the Arctic Sea. Its life is spent among the broken and floating ice offshore. The polar bear is the most aberrant of all the regular bears. It is a great hunter and to a great extent carnivorous, but in a time of necessity it will eat seaweeds, grasses, and roots as well as any animal substance that comes within its reach. Its favorite foods, however, are seals, walruses, stranded whales, fishes, and crustaceans. Although classed as a land animal, it is the only bear that is aquatic.

Scarcely superseded in size by the big brownie, it averages between seven to eight feet in length and 900 pounds in weight—and individuals have weighed up to three-quarters of a ton.

The polar bear is especially interesting as it does not follow the usual way of life expected of it. In the water it can swim from three to six miles per hour. Only the forelimbs and great paws are used to propel it along while the hindlimbs are carried straight out behind—a singular peculiarity that is not shared by any of the other four-footed land animals. It was probably through some similar effect of evolution that seals eventually lost the use of their hindlimbs. It is not unusual to find polar bears 70 to 80 miles from land and they have been seen on floating ice 200 miles offshore.

Monarch of the North, the polar bear lives in a strange, cold, bleak world of extremes. The dawn of one long continuous arctic summer day breaks in March, after a long period of darkness, intense cold, and bitter winds of the arctic winter. More than any creature, it would seem that the polar bear would adhere to the family habit of hibernation and thus escape the cold, lean winter months, but it does not. It is out hunting along the edge of the ice when many other animals are snug in their dens.

The wonders of this remarkable creature do not end here. When the female is going to have a family, she goes ashore on solid land. There she dens up for the winter in true bruin style—but she does so only in those winters when she is going to be a mother, or has the care of the family, usually twins. The alternate winters she turns to the happy hunting grounds where fat seals climb up on the floating ice. (*See also Mammal*) —G.G.G.

Recommended Reading

Field Book of North American Mammals—H. E. Anthony. G. P. Putnam's Sons, New York.
Lives of Game Animals—Ernest Thompson Seton. Doubleday, Doran & Company, Inc., New York.
The Mammals of Connecticut—George G. Goodwin. Bulletin No. 53, State Geological and Natural History Survey. Hartford, Connecticut.
The Mammal Guide—Ralph S. Palmer. Doubleday & Company, Inc., Garden City, New York.
Mammals of North America—Victor H. Cahalane. The Macmillan Company, New York.
Review of Grizzly and Brown Bears of North America—C. Hart Merriam.
North American Fauna, No. 41—Bureau of Biological Survey, Washington, D.C.

BEAR RIVER MIGRATORY BIRD REFUGE

Location—The shore of Great Salt Lake, Utah
Size—101 square miles
Mammals—Beavers, coyotes, muskrats, weasels, skunks, rabbits, hares
Birdlife—Many species of ducks and geese, four species of gulls; terns, herons,

Polar bears

chucks, gophers and pocket mice, and, to a lesser extent, to the fieldmice, muskrats, and porcupines. Most rodents are relatively small mammals, so that the beaver, with an average weight of about 40 pounds, is a giant among its fellows. It is the largest of all North American rodents, and in size it is exceeded only by the South American capybara, the largest rodent in the world.

The beaver is a chunky animal with dark brown back and sides, and with somewhat lighter underparts. It has a large, deep head with small, rounded ears—which nevertheless are prominent, particularly when the animal is swimming. In the front of the mouth are very strong, chisel-shaped incisor teeth, two above and two below, which serve as the tools and weapons for this animal. These teeth are noticeable, not only because of their large size but also because of their yellow color. The forefeet of the beaver are rather small and clawed; they are very mobile and serve as rather efficient hands. The hindfeet are large and have webs between the toes—obviously to propel the animal through the water. Perhaps the most characteristic external feature of the beaver is the broad, flat, trowel-shaped tail, virtually naked of hair and covered with overlapping scales.

This peculiar tail, so characteristic of the beaver and so different from the tails of other mammals, has been a subject of discussion since time immemorial, and numerous and fantastic legends have grown up as to its uses. Perhaps the commonest belief is that the beaver uses its tail as a trowel, to shape and pat down mud on the surface of its dam or lodge. As a matter of fact, no such wonderful and specialized skill is inherent in the tail of the beaver, and it functions much as do the tails in other mammals. The tail is used in swimming to control the direction in which the animal is moving, and to some extent as an aid in propulsion. On land it serves as a prop to the beaver when it stands on its hind legs. Functioning in this man-

The beaver feeds on tender bark

ner, the tail is very useful, for the beaver spends a great deal of its time in an erect or semi-erect position. Occasionally the tail is used for carrying mud and sticks. Observers who have seen the beaver use its tail in this fashion say that it is usually curved underneath the body, so that the articles being carried are clasped between the tail and the abdomen. Finally, the tail is used to slap the water just as the beaver dives beneath the surface. This slap by the tail—and it is a very loud, sharp sound—serves as a warning to other beavers that danger is imminent. So when a beaver dives with a loud slap of his tail, there usually follows a series of slaps from other beavers in the vicinity, and almost immediately all of the animals have disappeared from view.

Originally the American beaver, *Castor canadensis*, was widespread throughout North America north of Mexico, but constant trapping and shooting have so decimated the ranks of this once prolific animal that today only scattered colonies exist south of Canada. In the Canadian woods the beaver is still numerous, but even here the numbers are diminishing in the face of extensive trapping. It is difficult to say how many beavers lived in North America prior to the coming of the white man, but conservative estimates place the number at no less than 60 million, and more probably at 100 million.

The tender bark of trees, preferably aspen, cottonwood, and willow, forms the bulk of the beaver's diet. It is not unusual, however, for the beaver to feed on the bark of other trees, especially pine. In the summer, grass may be eaten to a limited extent. This animal is a strict vegetarian and it never eats fish as so many people believe.

The beaver is especially noted for its great skill as an engineer. The structures this animal builds are truly remarkable, not only for their size and for the skill with which they are built but also for the manner in which they are adapted to their surroundings. There are three principle types of beaver structures: the dam, the house or lodge, and the canal.

The beaver dam is usually built across a stream of constantly flowing water. The beavers begin to make a dam by piling branches and small logs across the stream, with the sticks ordinarily arranged so that they are longitudinal to the current. They pack this layer down with mud and stones. On this layer of sticks and mud a second layer of sticks, similarly weighed and packed down, is placed. The process is repeated until the dam reaches the desired height. Then, by assiduous packing on the part of the beavers and partly as the result of natural silting by the stream, the dam soon becomes watertight.

Beaver dams are seldom more than four to five feet high, but they may vary in length from a few feet to more than half a mile. They may be straight or curved. When curved, the shape is always haphazard, never scientifically designed as is often stated by careless observers.

The purpose of the beaver dam is to form a pond in which the beaver can live. In or on the edge of this pond the beaver constructs its lodge, and near the lodge it stores its supply of food for the winter. This food supply is a great mass of young trees and branches, weighted with stones and mud so that it sinks to the bottom. When the pond freezes, the food supply is beneath the ice but accessible to the beaver in its lodge.

The lodge is usually a dome-shaped structure with thick walls built of interlacing sticks and mud. Ordinarily it is in the middle of the pond, entirely surrounded by water, but often lodges are built on the edge of the pond, contiguous to the bank. The lodge contains a room, or sometimes several rooms, with a shelflike floor above water level. The entrances to the lodge, of which there may be several, are always under the water. Usually they are near the bottom of the pond so that they will be completely free of ice in the winter. Inside the lodge, protected by thick walls and by underwater entrances, the beaver family is safe from almost all of its numerous enemies except man.

Beavers build their canals for various reasons. Usually they are for the purpose of floating logs and branches into the pond. Such canals ordinarily are dug from the edge of the pond toward a grove of trees. If the land rises steeply, the canal continues only to such a distance as is feasible. From its end to the grove, a roadway or slide is formed, along which the logs are dragged or rolled into the canal. Canals are sometimes dug to connect two ponds, and occasionally a canal may be constructed to divert water from a stream into a pond. The canals are commonly about 15 inches in depth and from 15 to 18 inches in width, while in length they range from a few feet up to six or seven hundred feet.

The economic importance of beavers is and has been of inestimable value. In fact, the trade in beaver skins formed a basis for the early settlement of North America, and the history of Canada particularly has paralled the traffic in beavers. New Amsterdam, which later was to become New York, was founded as a trading post, the most important commodity of which was beaver pelts. Today the beaver is no longer important as a fur-bearing animal in the United States, but in Canada it is still being trapped in considerable numbers. Perhaps the beaver's greatest value at the present time is in the important and coincidental contribution that it makes to flood control. In mountainous districts beaver ponds do much to equalize the volume of stream flow, preventing serious washouts in times of torrential rains and acting as storage reservoirs in times of drought. —E.H.C.

Recommended Reading

American Mammals—W. J. Hamilton, Jr. McGraw-Hill Book Company, New York.
Mammals of North America—Victor H. Cahahane. The Macmillan Company, New York.
World of the Beaver—Leonard Lee Rue, III. J. B. Lippincott Company.

Beavers dam streams, often causing them to flood part of the surrounding area

The perfectly hexagonal compartments of the honeybee's cone are built of beeswax

BEE

These insects are members of the order Hymenoptera, which also includes the ants and the wasps. All species in this group have two pairs of wings in the adult form. (Worker ants are undeveloped females.) Each species has complete metamorphosis, wherein the individual passes through the egg and the larval state before finally becoming an adult.

Bees differ from ants and wasps in a number of ways; one of the most important is in the adaptations of the mouthparts. Where some ants and wasps are flesh eaters and have chewing mandibles and short tongues, the vegetarian bees have weaker mandibles but very long tongues, necessary tools for probing the tubes of deep-throated flowers. Bees are unique in the possession of pollen baskets, a fringe of hair on each hind leg that is used to transport pollen.

The eyes of bees are large and compound, composed of many facets, each one a register of light intensity. Bees can perceive large shapes, but their power of resolution, of sharpness of vision, is far inferior to that of humans. Their color vision is good; although they cannot distinguish red from black, they can see ultraviolet, a color that is beyond the range of the human eye. They do not have ears, and do not react to sounds. Their sense of smell is quite keen, and is located on the antennae; these organs can smell, taste, and feel.

Bees feed upon nectar and pollen, digesting it into honey. Stored in caves, hollow trees, or man-made hives, this product is relished by other insects, some birds, and many mammals, including, of course, man. But the service of the bees is far greater than merely that of producing honey. In the process of gathering nectar, they inadvertently transfer pollen from plant to plant of the same species, thus insuring cross-pollinization and the development of fruit and seeds.

Most species of bees are not social (the honeybee is an exception); that is, the daughters hatch out, fly away, mate, and begin their own families. Among truly social insects, few females lay eggs; the great majority of them are workers that spend their short lives working for the interests of the hive by collecting food, caring for the young, and expanding the nest or hive. Males and fully sexed females are hatched from special eggs during a definite season; among most social insects the young queens and the males mate and fly away. With the honeybee, the mated female may return and replace her own mother.

Solitary bees are divided into a roughly equal number of males and females. The mated female builds a nest, places pollen and honey in the nest chamber, then deposits an egg. In most species, she then walls off the chamber, brings in more pollen, and lays another egg, continuing until the chamber is filled. A few species are parasitic, laying eggs in the nests of others. —G.B.S.

Bumblebee
Other Common Names—Humblebee
Scientific Name—*Bombus americanorum*
Family—Apidae (carpenter bees, bumblebees, honeybees, and allies)
Order—Hymenoptera
Size—Length, about one inch
Range—United States, abundant in the eastern Central States; also in southern Canada

Members of the genus *Bombus* are social bees. In fact, since the honeybee is not native, bumblebees of the genus *Bombus* are the only native bees of this country that are truly social. By "social" is meant that they live in a colony consisting of a mother (the queen) and her offspring. Some of the daughters do most

The antennae of the bumblebee, like those of other bees, are sensory organs

of the work in the colony (hence are called workers) and do not mate.

Unlike the honeybee, a colony of *Bombus* bees does not continue year after year. In late summer all die except the young queens. These mate and crawl into some safe retreat, usually underground. The next year they emerge and each, often rather leisurely, starts to establish a new colony. Most species like to find a deserted nest of a mouse or chipmunk, preferably on or under the ground, the choice differing according to the species of *Bombus*. Having located a suitable place, the queen makes a honey pot out of wax and fills it with honey. She also makes a waxen cell in which she lays a few eggs, usually after having stocked it with some pollen mixed with honey.

When the grublike larvae hatch, each eats its way into the food. In doing so it makes a hollow that serves as its cradle. While this is going on, the queen mother stays home most of the time. She sips from her honey pot and occasionally pays attention to her growing young and feeds them a bit. The details vary with the species.

When fully grown, each larva spins its own cocoon within which it pupates. About three weeks after the egg is laid a mature bee crawls out of its pupal cocoon, soon to be ready to start its work of caring for its future sisters and, toward the end of the season, its brothers. After getting the colony started, the queen does little but lay eggs and usually not very much of that. In the first part of the season the offspring are workers, but about the time that males are born there are also young females

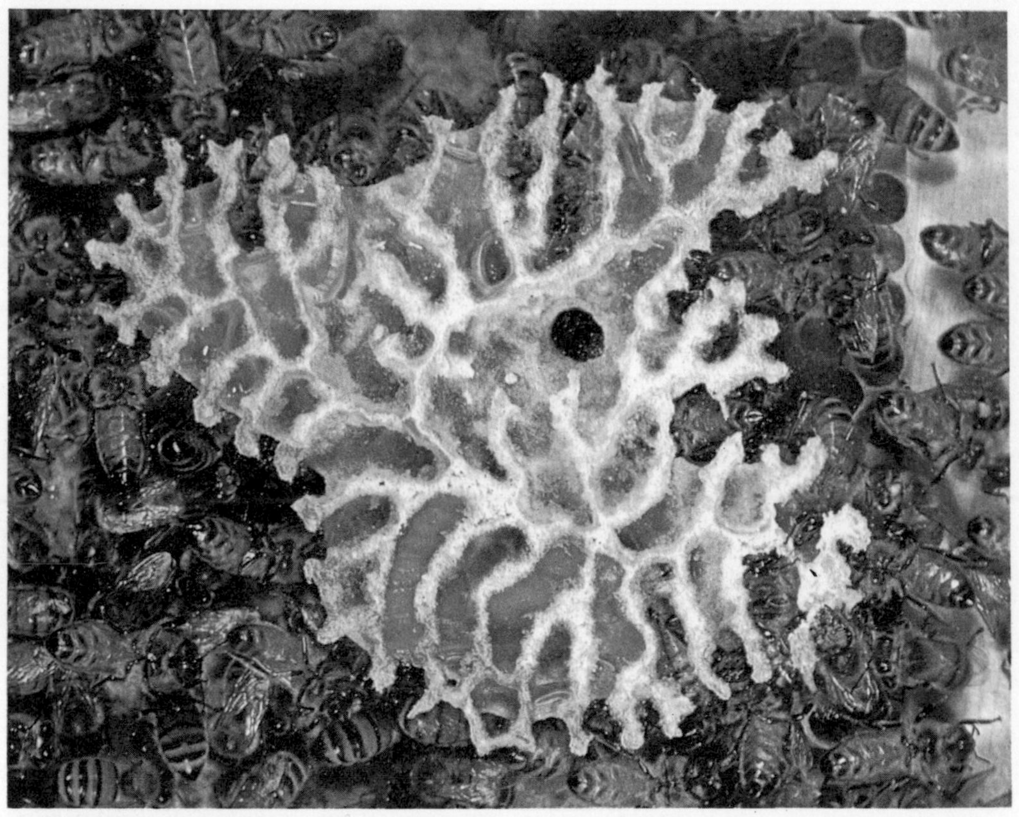

Magnified view of a spur comb

that will mate and repeat the cycle of colony formation and death.

The Parasitic Bumblebees

The distant ancestors of the parasitic genus *Psithyrus* were undoubtedly industrious bumblebees that scientists might classify as *Bombus*, but several things happened. Which happened first scientists do not know. Possibly they all took place gradually and at the same time. At any rate, the females of *Psithyrus* now have no pollen-carrying concavity on their hind legs; they do not collect pollen; there are no workers; and the females do not make nests and raise young but get into the nests of their relatives and let the workers of the industrious *Bombus* do it for them.

Although scientists do not know definitely which happened first, there is one fact that is suggestive. Sometimes a real *Bombus* queen that has not yet started a colony will, on finding a colony that has been started, go in and make herself at home. Such action may have been the first step that led to *Psithyrus*. Generation after generation they became more and more addicted to depending on others. Not only did the mothers lose the habit of gathering pollen to feed their children, but it came about that none of their children were workers—all were merely reproducers and they even lost the concavity on the hind legs that was used to carry pollen. Now they cannot work if they want to. They are social parasites.

With the reference to social values, perhaps a word should be added concerning the great benefit that the industrious *Bombus* bumblebees are to all parts of the world that they inhabit. Their activity in flying from flower to flower in search of nectar and pollen results in the pollination of the flowers and, hence, the formation of seeds. Since bumblebees have long, slim tongues, they can reach the nectar even of red clover. In fact, were it not for their visits, this highly important plant and

Queen bumblebee

Male bumblebee

Worker bumblebee

Right wing of bumblebee (enlarged)

Right wing of carpenter bee (enlarged)

some of its relatives would set practically no seed. Of course, *Psithyrus* is very little help in this. *Xylocopa* (carpenter bees) have a neat trick that benefits it but not the rest of the world. If it cannot reach the nectar at the base of a tubular flower in the regular way, it bites a hole in the side of the flower and gets at it in that way. Some bumblebees with relatively short tongues also make forcible entrances into the nectaries of flowers in this way. —F.E.L.

Recommended Reading

Bumblebees and Their Ways—O. E. Plath. Macmillan Company.
Field Book of Insects—Frank E. Lutz. G. P. Putnam's Sons.

Great Carpenter Bee
Other Common Names—None
Scientific Name—*Xylocopa virginica*
Family—Apidae (carpenter bees, bumblebees, honeybees, and allies)
Order—Hymenoptera
Size—Length, one inch
Range—In eastern and southern North America, the great carpenter bee, *X. virginica,* is the most common species. Carpenter bees are restricted to a few genera and to 350 species in the world. They are widely distributed in forested areas of warmer regions. In the tropics more than 300 species are known. There are said to be 3 species in Central America, 3 in Australia, 18 in India, and 26 in North America

The large family Apidae includes, the carpenter bees, bumblebees, honeybees, and others. With a few exceptions, such as the "cuckoo" bees that leave the care and feeding of their offspring to others, these insects are models of industry. Not without reason has the saying, "busy as a bee," been applied to people who are particularly hard working.

To judge by the task it undertakes to shelter its young—that of boring tunnels in dry wood—one of the hardest working members of this big family is *Xylocopa*, represented over much of the United States by the species *X. virginica.* Because of its woodworking habits, it is often called "carpenter bee;" this name is also given to a race of much smaller bees, Ceratinidae, which chew into the pithy stems of plants to make their nests.

However, there is no mistaking these two species of "carpenters," since *X. virginica* is as large as the largest bumblebee. In fact, it bears such a resemblance to a bumblebee that it is frequently mistaken for one. This is especially so when the woodworker has been tumbling about in flower pollen, as it often does, and has its shining black, almost hairless abdomen well dusted with pollen gold. Also, at such times it is not easy to notice that the carpenterbee has a much flatter body than a bumblebee.

The carpenter bee, *Xylocopa*, differs from *Bombus*, the bumblebees, in other ways. First, bumblebees are social insects, with several bees or more working together for the welfare of the colony. *Xylocopa*, on the other hand, is what is termed a solitary bee, with each female being both queen and worker. At the beginning of winter both sexes go into hibernation to be ready to start a new generation the following summer, but with bumblebees only the fertilized queens survive.

Although bumblebees build their nests in pre-made holes in the ground, in abandoned mouse nests or those made by birds, or even under old papers in vacant buildings, the carpenter bee selects a site usually on the underside of a log, a barn timber, or other dry and solid wood. There she begins her nest tunnel, her only excavating tool being her strong jaws, or mandibles, which she uses most skillfully.

It appears that the female carpenter follows a plan for her tunnels that is as old as her race, for they have "drift" and "run" after the best mining methods. In selecting the underside of timbers, not only does she thus prevent rain from entering her tunnels, but she facilitates the removal of excavated materials. The force of gravity is her assistant in the work.

The bee bores a hole about as large as that made by a 45-caliber bullet. She works at right angles to the grain of the wood to a point equal to her length and then she turns either right or left, sometimes completing one tunnel in each direction. Occasionally she will cross the grain for another body length and then make a second tunnel parallel to the first. Her rate of burrowing with the grain has been timed at half-an-inch a day. The crossgrain work is much slower, but no doubt the texture of the wood determines her progress.

Now comes the task of "furnishing" the new home. Within it she makes a pellet of flower pollen, cemented together with nectar, that resembles a small section of art-gum. The queen lays a single egg upon the mass. Then she moves toward the tunnel opening and builds a wall-partition of wood fragments and saliva that seals off her first cell. Then she deposits another pollen

A carpenter bee pauses at its nest door

pellet, another egg, and builds another partition. Each cell is a little less than an inch long. In this way she fills her wooden galleries with ten or more "bed-chambers," into each of which she places an egg and enough nourishment to last the hatchling through its larval period, after which it will pupate into adulthood.

During this process, which may take the queen carpenter several weeks since all the eggs must be laid about the same time, the larvae are always about the same size. Were this not true, the

A cross-section of a decayed log shows the structure of the carpenter bee's nest

first emerging adult, traveling from the farther end of the burrow toward the entrance, would play havoc with its brothers and sisters that had a later start in life.

What of the male carpenter bee? In the economy of nature, these male bees, distinguished by a white spot on their foreheads that is lacking on their spouses, apparently live without work. Like the drones of the honeybee hives they have but one mission in life; having attended to it, they are at liberty to sip nectar to their gullet's capacity. Sometimes, in late summer, a single male will be seen hanging about a nest's tunnel entrance, watching for any newly-emerged females.

After her last cell is provisioned and sealed, the hard-working female carpenter bee may, if life and time will permit, go in for a bit of "sky-larking." In sipping nectar from such flowers as those that open on the passion vine (Passiflora), she becomes well dusted with pollen for which she now has no need. Apparently this is uncomfortable and displeasing, for she has been observed making strenuous efforts to remove the pollen from her person. To do this "dry cleaning," the carpenter female hangs herself from a weed branch or vine with her front feet (sometimes supported by a single foot). Then she combs the gold dust from her body by her legs or tarsi. Not until she is quite free of this accumulation does she fly away.

While the species of these larger carpenter bees in North America are few, they increase in number the nearer one gets to the tropics. They also grow more colorful. While many are jet-black, some are blue with a metallic sheen. Others—according to C. H. Curran in his book, *Insects of the Pacific World*—have bright-colored hairs over their thorax and first segment. He writes that one of these species, the gorgeous *Xylocopa coerulea*, occurs in the East Indies and has a thorax thickly covered with hairs of a sky-blue color. Curran also adds the information that the female of a certain tropical carpenter bee has an aperture in its "first segment that leads to a chamber known as a 'mite pocket' because it constitutes a favorite gathering place for mites."

The woodworking bees add a goodly share of interest for all those interested in nature, and their multitudes do much to enliven the earth with their diverse and busy lives. —R.J.D. and M.L.D.

Honeybee
Other Common Names—Hive bee
Scientific Name—*Apis mellifera*
Family—Apidae (carpenter bees, bumblebees, honeybees, and allies)
Order—Hymenoptera
Size—Length, one-half inch
Range—Entire United States and southern Canada

The honeybee, *Apis mellifera*, is only one of many thousands of species of bees that are fellow denizens of the earth but, due to the useful role it plays in the affairs of men and its consequent wide domestication, it is the bee that above all others is of interest to mankind. Strictly speaking this bee is an alien—although a very desirable one.

Honey was always relished in the western hemisphere, but it was honey produced by the stingless bees of the tropics that, to this day, in the wild state or sometimes domesticated, furnish honey to Central and South Americans. The honeybee, of Old World origin, was introduced into New England around 1638.

It is not unusual to think of the honeybee colony as a state and, at a time when monarchies were the predominant type of state, the individual of greatest stature in the bee colony came to be designated as the king. Subsequently this royal member was detected in the unkingly act of egg-laying and so it was necessary to recognize the supposed ruler of the colony as a queen. Queen is the name that has persisted not only with the honeybee, but also for individuals of more or less corresponding function in other genera of social bees. It is also applied to the social wasps, the ants, and the termites. The name, however, is misleading. The so-called queen of the honeybees is not a ruler; she is the slave of her own limiting instincts, destined—except for the occasion when she issues forth on her mating flight, or when, after a long interval of incarceration, she accompanies a swarm from the parent hive to a new hive—to spend her life in the dark recesses of her home, egg-laying to the number of about 1,500 to 2,000 eggs per day under normal conditions at the peak of her oviposting.

In view of this great fecundity—incidentally persisted in over a period ordinarily of three or four years, although there is normally only a single act of copulation—the colony is not deficient in numbers. Although the life of an adult worker bee in the nectar-gathering season is only about six weeks, new adults are constantly emerging and a colony may, at its peak of population, approximate 70,000. Even such a colony, however, may shrink to 10,000 individuals or less by the close of winter.

The ordinarily sterile workers, even though they are incapable of mating, may, under certain circumstances carry out the function of egg-laying. If a colony, for instance, is deprived of its queen, the workers sometimes take over her task. But the eggs they lay, being unfertilized, develop only into males and, as a colony in order to flourish must have a continual supply of new workers to replace those who die, the queenless colony is doomed unless a new queen is reared.

The hive as a family flourishes when a mother and an adequate number of daughters are functioning. But the pres-

The honeybee has special hairs, or scopa, on its hind legs for collecting pollen

ence of grandchildren, the emergency progeny of the workers, instead of being an indication of family prosperity and continuity, may be a sign of the impending dissolution of the hive.

Instead of regarding the colony as a state or as a family, one may take the somewhat startling viewpoint that it is a single organic whole comprised of components of varied function. The human body, in spite of its unity, is an aggregate of cells of very diverse responsibilities. Some of these cells—like the red blood corpuscles, for instance—even lead a more or less detached and independent existence, traveling extensively throughout the system while on their task of carrying vital cargoes of oxygen to parts of the body where the oxygen is needed. Other cells have more

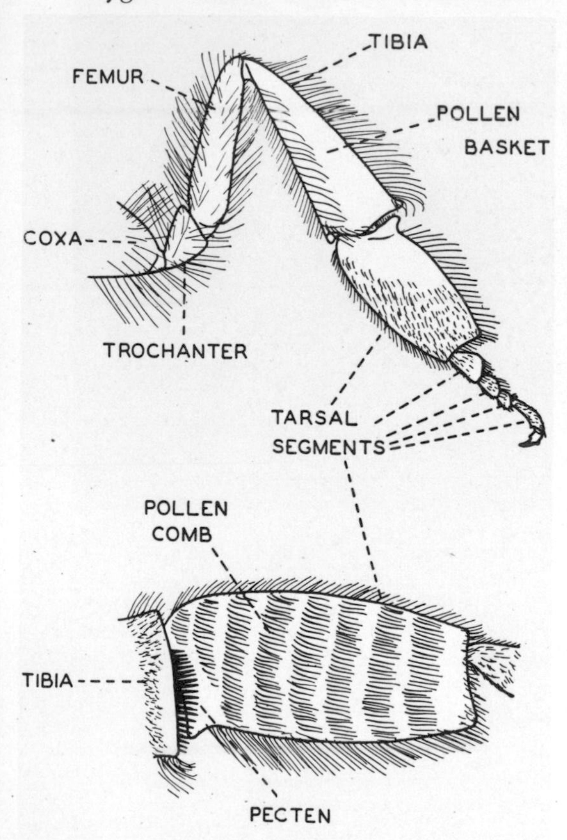

Hind leg of worker honeybee

localized functions. One may see in this some parallelism, even if remote, to the well organized unity of the hive, in which there is such interdependence, due to specialized structure and correlated function among the different castes, that individuals are virtually incapable of survival except as members of the whole.

The male is a relatively useless member of the honeybee cooperative effort. His sole function is to fertilize the queen and, so that this end may be achieved, many of his kind are produced, only to be driven ultimately from the hive and either slaughtered or left to starve. This helpless member of the community is, like the queen and the larvae of all castes, dependent on the workers for its food.

The workers perform the multifarious tasks of the hive, involving building, storing, feeding, cleaning, ventilating (through fanning with their wings), regulating temperature (through muscular activity), and guarding the portals. They are its masons, its charwomen, its nursery brigade, its provision gatherers, and its defenders. At first all the tasks of the adult worker are indoor tasks; only in the later weeks of her life is this individual a forager, ranging the meadows in search of floral food over distances that may extend to several miles.

Even the indoor tasks follow a certain sequence dependent on the age of the individual. Thus the wax which constitutes the building material of the cells is secreted by glands on the underside of the abdomen chiefly during a certain stage of the worker's life, and such comb-building as is required in the hive is performed usually only by bees in this secreting stage. The pharyngeal glands, however, function at an earlier stage than the wax-producing glands and the significance of the product of these glands – royal jelly – deserves special mention.

One of the many marvels associated with the colony is the rearing of the larvae, the babyhood stage of the bee. Royal jelly is fed to all castes—queen, worker, drone—during the first two or three days of their larval life. However, if a female larva is to be reared as a worker, that diet is then changed to honey and pollen, as is also done in the case of the male. A female larva that is to be reared as a queen is fed royal jelly up to the time of her pupation. It is not due to a difference in the egg or in the larva, nor to differences in environment, such as that presented by the hexagonal worker's cell and the peanutlike royal cell, that the destiny of the larva is decided. It is the character of the food alone that determines whether she is to emerge as a queen or as a commoner.

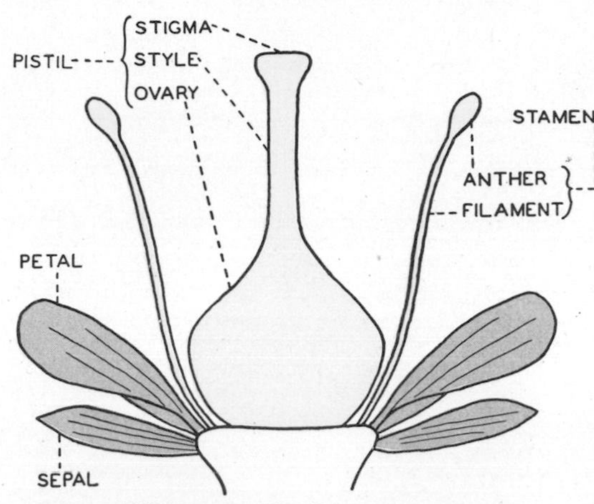

Diagram of a flower

In the field a given individual honeybee on one of its flights is apt to confine its visits to definite species of flowers. This is of advantage to the bee, for familiarity with the floral architecture of a given species of plant assures quick access to the nectaries (the source of honey) and saves effort and time. It is likewise of advantage to the plant which is dependent for its pollination upon bees that carry pollen loads from plant to plant of the same species. But how do the bees recognize the plants of a particular species?

Thanks to the experiments of Professor von Frisch, more is now known re-

A honeybee alights on a thistle blossom

garding the senses of bees and the part they play in these floral quests. It is known that the bees have a sense of color, even though they are unable to distinguish as many color shades as man does, tending to confuse blue with purple and violet, and orange with yellow. They are color-blind to red, being unable to differentiate it from black. By way of offset, they can see what man cannot see – ultraviolet. Their color blindness to red explains the virtual absence in nature of red flowers that are also bee flowers. When a red flower, like the poppy, proves the rare exception of being attractive to bees, the explanation is that the poppy reflects ultraviolet, and in consequence has a significance for the bee quite apart from the unrecognized red coloration.

Even more influential in flower selection than color discrimination is the sense of smell. When a foraging bee visits a flower in quest of nectar, the scent of the flower clings to the hairs and body surfaces of the insect. If the nectar supply is abundant, the bee on its return to the hive circles about with vigor, and by these antics attracts the attention of the other bees. These become excited, approach the gyrating bee, follow her about, keep their antennae (in which the sense of smell is located) close to the body of the performer and, after having familiarized themselves with the specific odor of the plant that she has been visiting, fly out in turn to locate plants from which a like odor is emanating. If they are successful in this quest for nectar, they will on their return to the hive perform the dance and thus incite ever increasing numbers of the bee community to set forth on the profitable quest.

The time comes, however, when the well-supplied blooms have been largely robbed of their liquid treasures and the visits of the bees yield only diminishing returns. There is no longer good news to spread throughout the hive. The returning bees show no inclination to circle about in their peculiar dance. The excitement dies down. Far from being a disadvantage, however, this succeeding apathy is a real service. It prevents the bees from going forth on relatively useless missions, holding them in check until some discoverer of a new source of nectar bears the exciting message to the hive by engaging in the characteristic dance. This interesting means of communicating essential information is often referred to as "the language of the bees." (*See under Animal: Animal Navigation*)

Man's debt to the honeybee cannot find adequate expression. From the beginnings of human history to the present, man has enjoyed honey. There is even a rock painting at the Cuevas de la Arana, northwest of Biscorp, Valencia, Spain, that is believed to represent a gatherer of wild honey in prehistoric times. Honey is mentioned in the Sumerian and Babylonian cuneiform writings. Beekeeping was known to the ancient Egyptians, even to the inclusion of some of the refinements of the art. For instance, certain of the tricks of apiculture that the uninitiated are apt to think of as brand new, such as the removal of hives from region to region in order to take advantage of the nectar flow, were known to the dwellers of the Nile region at least as long ago as the third century before Christ.

There are many delectable kinds of honey, depending on the blossoms from which the nectar is derived. White clover honey is known to everyone and is relished by all, but many other plants yield a toothsome product through the agency of the bees. Praise has been bestowed upon the honey derived from acacias, alfalfa, apple, Canada thistle, citrus fruits – the source frequently of "orange honey" – clematis, gallberry, locust, manzanita, mesquite, sages, wild raspberry, and many other plants. Certain kinds of honey are valued particularly for baking. Buckwheat honey is used in this way and one might mention

A swarm of bees

several others, such as the honey extracted from the partridge pea and from ti-ti or leatherwood. In addition to honey, beeswax has been a great boon to man and it has been used in many different ways.

It is in pollinating plants, however, that the honeybee renders its major service. Many diverse floral structures are visited by this persistent searcher for nectar and pollen, and wherever the bee derives benefit from a plant, it is apt automatically to reward its benefactor by acting as an agent of fertilization, thus assuring the perpetuation of the plant species from which it has taken a moderate toll. The blooms visited include those of important forage plants and those of favored orchard fruits, as well as those of a number of plants that through their beauty or even just because they are part of the familiar environment are a source of pleasure to man. It is true that many a plant that is frequented by the honeybee is attractive also to wild bees of other species, but the populous colonies of the honeybee can be relied upon numerically to assure pollination where the sparser representation of native bee species might sometimes fail in amply fulfilling the task. The fact that many an orchardist installs hives of the honeybee for the sake of the apple crop rather than for the yield of honey is an indication of the high rating given to this bee as an aid in horticulture. (*See also under Pollination*)

Only the workers and the queen are armed with a sting, and the queen usually reserves her weapon for use against a royal rival. Because it is unpleasant to be stung, the chimerical suggestion has sometimes been made that by crossing the honeybee with one of the stingless bees of the tropics, there might be developed a bee of innocuous behavior but retaining all the virtues of the hon-

The honeybee is invaluable to man as a pollinator of flowers

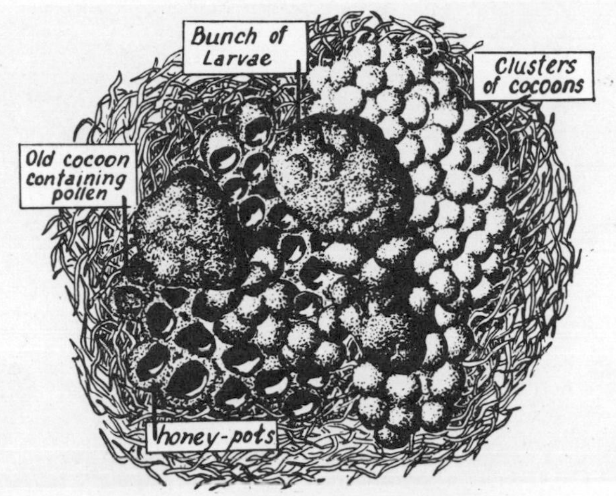

Nest of a bumblebee in midsummer

eybee. Such a union would be inconceivable in a state of nature. Even if it were achieved through artificial insemination, one wonders at the strange progeny that would result and at the confusion of habits that might be the heritage, for the two groups of bees are in several respects divergent from each other. The stingless bees build their combs horizontally, the honeybee builds them vertically. In the case of the stingless bees, the cells face upward and consist of a single layer of cells per comb, while in the honeybee they are placed laterally and one layer of cells is backed by a second layer of cells facing in the opposite direction from the first layer. The stingless bees store their honey and pollen in specially constructed jars, often arranged in clusters, the honeybee stores its provisions in combs.

When a swarm of stingless bees sets out from the parental nest to establish itself elsewhere, it is one of the royal daughters that takes part in the exodus, while the old queen enacts this role in the case of the honeybee. Perhaps the most fundamental divergence of all is the manner of feeding the larvae. The stingless bees provide all the nutriment intended for the larva before the egg from which it will emerge is laid and then close the cell, leaving the larva to feed on the gathered store. The honeybee larva, on the other hand, is fed throughout its entire development by attendant workers and is sealed off only when it no longer requires this care. These differences notwithstanding, the stingless bees are probably the closest living relatives of the honeybee and its affiliates in the genus *Apis*. —H.F.S.

Recommended Reading

American Social Insects—Charles D. and Mary H. Michener. D. Van Nostrand Company, Inc., New York.

The Anatomy of the Honey Bee—R. E. Snodgrass. Cornell University Press. Ithaca, New York.

Beekeeping—Everett Franklin Phillips. The Macmillan Company, New York. Rev. ed.

Bees and Wasps—Oswald H. Latter. Cambridge University Press, New York.

Bees: Their Vision, Chemical Senses, and Language—Karl von Frisch. Cornell University Press, Ithaca, New York. (paperback ed.)

A Book About Bees—Edwin Way Teale. Indiana University Press. Paperback. Originally published as **The Golden Throng**, Dodd, Mead and Company, New York.

The Dancing Bees—Karl von Frisch. Harcourt, Brace & Company, Inc., New York.

Honeybee—Mary Adrian. Holiday House, New York.

The Life of the Bee—Maurice Maeterlinck. Dodd, Mead & Company, New York. (Paperback ed., New American Library)

M. H. BEVANS

BEECH
American Beech
Other Common Names—None
Scientific Name—*Fagus grandifolia*
Family—Fagaceae (beech family)
Range—Nova Scotia west to southern Ontario; Maine to central Wisconsin, south to eastern Texas and northern Florida
Habitat—Prefers moist or even wet soils with good drainage, such as slopes above a lake or swamp
Leaves—Three to six inches long, rather shiny and either broadly or narrowly lance-shaped; usually with a fairly long point and singly toothed margins, much resembling the longer leaf of the American chestnut to which it is related. Winter buds are very narrow, long (a full one-half inch), and sharply pointed
Bark—Very pale gray and smooth, with fine dark speckling and thin, split lines as though barely big enough for the tree. A smoky, dark tone is frequently noticeable on one side of the trunk, with still darker, cracked areas around the base
Flowers—Male: most noticeable are one inch, yellow-green "balls" hanging from rather limp stems right after the young leaves open
Fruit—Small prickly burs (about five-eighths of an inch long) that open to release two small three-sided nuts much sought as food (mast) by many birds—wild turkeys, wood ducks, and others, including the now extinct passenger pigeon

The beech, a tree of the deep forest, is often surrounded by oaks or maples but is set apart from these in small groups of its own kind. These homogeneous formations are generally attributed to the growth of saplings from the surface roots of larger beeches; the saplings eventually attain the size of the "parent" tree. The maximum measurements given for the beech are 120 feet for the height with a trunk diameter of four feet.

The American chestnut, *Castanea dentata,* a now virtually extinct species, is closely related to the beech. The two share similar leaf shapes and almost identical prickly burs that cover the nuts common to both. The burs open in the early autumn, and the chestnuts that fall from them to the ground are gathered by many animals—squirrels, grouse, jays, and wood ducks. They comprise a large portion of the wood duck's diet.

The beech and chestnut exhibit a further fellowship in range and habitat. Before the chestnut blight, that began in 1907 and greatly reduced the species, the beech and the chestnut shared the same geographical range (see range of beech mentioned above). The remnants of the American chestnut are now somewhat confined to the eastern and northern portions of the country, and more particularly along the Appalachian Mountains. In habitat, the beech and the chestnut appear to thrive under similar conditions and both are found growing on moist slopes and flats approaching swamps—the beech to a larger degree. Both species are also considered members of the original northeastern climax forest.

Beech wood is tight-grained, heavy, strong, and hard to split. The wood is used for chairs and furniture, flooring railroad ties, and because of its clean odor it is desirable for food boxes and barrels. Although the wood is strong, tough, and handsome, it warps easily and is not very durable. Beech bark is sometimes used as an ingredient in skin ointment. The nuts were once gathered for market, but fruiting is scarce except in the far North.

Winter identification of an older beech is readily made by observing its outstanding bark; younger beeches can be recognized by their gradually tapering, almost needle-pointed buds. These are deep red-brown and flecked with cream on the scale tips. —M.H.B.

American beech

BEETLE

Beetles belong to the order Coleoptera—the largest insect order, containing about a quarter of a million species, or 40 percent of all insects. Of this number some 25,000 species are known to inhabit North America. The order Coleoptera is divided into two subfamilies, the beetles composing the first, and the weevils, the second.

All beetles, including weevils, have chewing mouthparts; however, the weevils have their mouthparts drawn out to form a beaklike projection that gives them the appearance of sucking insects.

The great variety within the order Coleoptera has fitted some members of it for almost every possible habitat on earth, except the polar ice caps and the oceans. Beetles inhabit forests, grasslands, deserts, and freshwater lakes, ponds, and streams. Diets of the different species vary tremendously; fresh animal food, carrion, animal wastes, and plant material of all kinds are utilized, and a few species digest anything organic.

One characteristic possessed by all the coleopterans, and only by them, is the heavy, thickened front wings, or *elytra.* These are of the same texture as the rest of the body covering, which means they may be hard and shiny or else covered with hair, spines, or scales. In most species (those that have a functional pair of hindwings), the elytra meet at center of the back, covering the true wings and forming a proctive shell over the abdomen. In others (those that have lost their wings entirely), the elyctra may be fused along the back.

Beetles undergo four-stage, or complete, metamorphosis. The eggs hatch into larvae that grow to larger than adult size before pupating and emerging as adults. Sexes are usually similar, but in some species the males have larger mandibles and antennae, and longer legs. A few kinds have grotesque projections on the head or the back of no known function except perhaps to intimidate possible predators.

Beetles frequently compete with man for the same foods. Some kinds profit by the human habit of planting solid stands of tree or food crops, while others invade stores of grain and other plant products. These activities are actually the result of a successful adjustment of the insect to a habitat favorably modified for it by the activities of mankind. (*See also under Balance of Nature; and Insect*) —G.B.S.

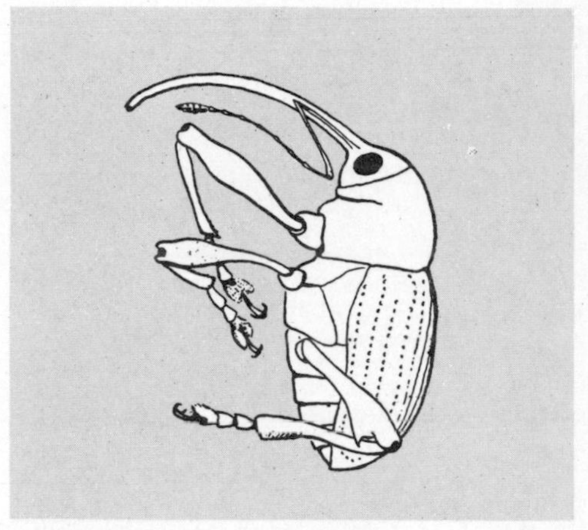

Weevils have chewing mouthparts enclosed in sharp, beaklike structures

May Beetle
Other Common Names—June bug, fruit beetle, figeater
Scientific Name—*Phyllophaga fusca*
Family—Scarabaeidae (May beetle family)
Order—Coleoptera
Size—Length, three-fourths of an inch
Range—Lives on the Atlantic slope and throughout the southern United States

One of summer's most interesting insects is the May beetle. Beetles belong to the order Coleoptera, which means *sheath-wings.* The hard, sheathlike wings of the May beetle are reddish-brown with tannish edges. As with all beetles, the hard outer wings form a protective covering for the thin, membranous, flying wing underneath.

It requires a three year cycle for the May beetle to reach its adult stage.

Eggs are laid by the female in tiny mud cases—one egg to each case—which she has formed into shape in a place just below the surface of the ground where the hatched grubs can find food. For three years after the grub hatches it lives underground and forages for its own food. It is a vegetarian, feeding upon all kinds of vegetable matter and plant roots, including seedling tobacco plants. White grubs below the ground in a field or garden can raise havoc with the roots of crops. Like all young and growing insects, the white grub has a voracious appetite. At the end of three years it reaches a length of two inches or more.

The May beetle undergoes a complete metamorphosis that is in four stages—egg, grub, pupa, and adult. When it is ready for the pupal stage, the grub makes a little clay pupal case and seals itself in. After a short period, averaging around two weeks, it emerges, a beautiful adult beetle. A certain number of May beetles emerge every spring with the various broods overlapping from year to year. The broods of some years are more numerous than others. For a brief time they fly through the warm summer evenings searching for ripe or decaying fruit for which they have a special fondness. Then they mate, lay their eggs, and die.

While the May beetle is in the immature, or grub stage, it belongs to the great horde of soil-forming burrowers and aids in the turnover of soil, bringing deeper soil near to the surface, pulverizing decaying vegetable matter, and adding to the fertilizer. In nature's scheme its job is important, but lest it become too numerous, there are checks to balance the economy of things—barring the interference of man.

Mammals that dig or burrow into the ground feed upon the May beetle grubs, for they are particularly fat and juicy morsels. Moles, shrews, and mice eat them, as do skunks, hogs, coyotes, badgers, bears, and, in the South, armadillos. Among the animals that destroy the adult beetles are birds, bats, and parasites.

The story of the May beetle's parasites is an interesting one. The May beetle is nocturnal and, like moths, it is attracted to artificial light. Unlike moths, however, it is more clumsy, and its flight around a light may well be its undoing. Flying among the beetles are small Pyrgota flies. A female selects a host beetle, and while its sheath wings are spread in flight, she swoops onto its unprotected back. Inserting her ovipostor in the soft back, she deposits her egg. Momentarily stunned, the beetle soon resumes its flight. For a few evenings it continues to fly, to search for food, and even to mate. But its movements become weaker, and it finally dies.

The Pyrgota fly's egg hatches and its grub feeds upon the beetle until it has consumed it. Then, inside the hollow shell of the beetle, it goes into its pupal stage. In some years there may be more Pyrgota flies than beetles, since the Pyrgota's life cycle is annual. In these years many of these parasitic flies die without finding hosts in which to deposit their eggs. Several tachinid fly species are also stealthy parasites upon the May beetle. These catch the beetle grub unaware and fasten their eggs to its body. The parasite of the immature, or white grub stage, is the thorny-headed worm. Its life cycle revolves between the May beetle grubs and swine.

At one time sugar cane plantations in the tropics suffered great losses from the encroachment of white grubs of another species of beetle. Their natural enemies there, the lizards and tree toads, were apparently too small to consume them in sufficient quantities. Adult giant Surinam toads, *Bufo marinus,* were imported, and within a number of years the populations of the grubs were much reduced.

Many beetles are vegetarians and are therefore often detrimental to crops, while some other beetle species, which are carnivorous, feed upon vegetable-eating

The May beetle spends three years underground before emerging as an adult

insects. Insecticides that destroy harmful insects, destroy friendly insects as well and are more or less dangerous to man. A better method that has been employed advantageously, especially in the control of insects of restricted food habits, is the rotation of crops resistant to the insect's attacks. Grubs of the May beetle, for example, feed largely on decaying vegetable matter but supplement this diet with roots of the grass family, such as forage grasses and grains. By rotating these crops with legumes, or using them in combination, root injuries by grubs are greatly reduced, since the grubs do not like legumes.

Crop resistance to insects is obtained by selection of resistant strains, by the importation of resistant varieties from abroad, by grafting, and by the crossing of plants to obtain desirable qualities. Examples of resistant strains are certain varieties of corn and sugar cane that will grow new roots to replace those eaten off by insects.

The order Coleoptera is the largest single order in the entire animal kingdom and the most widely distributed of the large orders of insects. More than 25,000 different species of beetles have been described in North America, and approximately 350,000 species for the world. The order includes some of the largest of insects and some of the smallest. It is said that the number and dominance of beetles is due to the protection afforded them by their hard, sheathlike wings. These, and a trick some of them have of feigning death, are some of their means of protection. Beetles invade land, air, and water in greater variety and numbers than any other insect order. Practically all of insects' diverse ways of feeding and living are practiced by beetles and their larvae.

The story of the May beetle may not be as exciting or romantic as that of some other insects, but it is curiously interesting. For example, the white grub does not crawl on its stomach as do other caterpillars. It flips over on its back and scoots along with surprising speed. The little clay case in which it seals itself before transforming into an adult beetle is the work of an expert potter. One cannot help but wonder at the instinct that guides it in its work of rounding off its earthen puparium and of making it exactly the right size. And the May beetle itself, is one of the prettiest of the harbingers of summer.

—I.S.